SO-CFL-383

The End of Diets:
Healing Emotional Hunger

Dilia De La Altagracia

Photography by Jeff Butler
Yoga model Nancy Nielsen

Copyright ©2003 Dilia De La Altagracia

This book is published by Applied Insight, Inc. No part of this book may be reproduced by any mechanical, photographic recording, nor may it be stored in retrieval system, transmitted, translated into another language, or otherwise copied for public or private use without the permission of the publisher, excepting brief passages quoted for purposes of critical review.

The author of this book does not presume to offer psychological therapy nor advocate the use of any technique for the treatment of any specific or traumatic psychological condition without the approval and guidance of a qualified psychotherapist. The intent of the author is to relate personal experience in the hope that it may be of help in our personal quest for permanent weight loss and the end of emotional eating. If you use any of the information or yoga postures are used as form of self-therapy, the author and publisher assume no responsibility for your actions.

First printing: November 2003
Second printing: January 2010
I.S.B.N. 0-9744092-0-0

Published by:
      Applied Insight, Inc.
      6354 S Lafayette Place
      Centennial, CO   80121
Visit our website: www.emotionalhunger.com

Library of Congress cataloging-in-publication data:

De La Altagracia, Dilia.
The End of Diets: Healing Emotional Hunger / Dilia De La Altagracia.

ISBN 0-9744092-0-0

1. Emotional Eating
2. Compulsive Eaters – Rehabilitation.
3. Self-help Techniques.
4. Food Habits
5. Psychological aspect
6. Psychology.
7. Emotions.
8. Yoga.
9. Meditation.
10. East/West Psychology.

contents

"There's a sun in every person – the you we call companion."

– Rumi

introduction

It is essential to realize and embrace the paradox that while no one can go through your journey for you, you are not alone. Many of us are on the parallel paths. We share similar pains, confusions, and fears — which, if shared between us, lose their edge and so cut us less.

A very touching story from the Talmud captures this soft paradox of how we all journey alone together. A rabbi asks his students, "How do you know the first moment of dawn has arrived?" After a great silence, one pipes up, "When you can tell the difference between a sheep and a dog." The rabbi shakes his head no. Another offers, "When you can tell the difference between a fig tree and an olive tree." Again, the rabbi shakes his head no. There are no other answers. The rabbi circles their silence and walks between them. "You know the first moment of dawn has arrived when you look into the eyes of another human being and see yourself."[1]

Although this story is my personal journey, it is a story that many people have experienced. The trek to a healthy, self-accepting body weight has become a struggle shared by many of us. We have tried the same diets, we have succumbed to this year's better and more elaborate marketing schemes, gone to the gym for months; we have hired the personal trainers, gone to Weight Watchers™, eating consultants, and nutritionists. In most cases we made some measurable progress, but most of the time these measurable gains have evaporated in less time than it took us to reach them. We then moved to more elaborate plans that might have included psychological help or specialized eating-disorder intervention. After experiencing many failures, I grew disillusioned. I began to understand that the percentage of people who fail at measurable achievements is colossal compared to those who achieve lifelong weight loss.

I was very blessed the day I was finally not seduced by the promises of the latest diet, not enticed by the newest piece of body shaping equipment, not moved by the next miracle weight loss pill. I began to see a pattern in myself that could only be called "emotional eating." My goal became to understand why emotional eating happens and — more important — how I could stop indulging this destructive behavior. My real achievement has been to understand what emotional eating is, how I acquired the ritual and how to, once and for all, recognize and override this dysfunctional behavior. I began to write about my pain and journey and found that friends and family found my insights useful in stopping their own emotional eating. I then understood that this was not only a story about me, or you, or just our friends; this is a story about us, a story that could change our lives and could help us stop emotional eating.

Being FAT in America is degrading, draining, shaming and finally debilitating. I remember when the decision to go anywhere was a function of how comfortable I would feel in my clothes. Places like the public swimming pool, dressy functions, elegant dinner parties, holiday galas, happy hour with the "beautiful people," skiing, long hikes, and single bars were completely out of the question, no longer considered. I just knew how difficult it was to get back up when I fell down skiing, how depressed I felt when not one lonely guy would speak to me at a singles event, how ashamed I felt looking at myself when I was wearing an elegant evening gown that fitted poorly.

And it was not just that I wanted to look attractive, the quality of my life was severely compromised. Health risks increase when we are overweight. We are twice as likely to develop diabetes, high blood pressure, heart disease, stroke, certain types of cancer, gout (joint pain caused by excess uric acid), gallbladder dysfunction, sleep apnea (interrupted breathing during sleep), and osteoarthritis (wearing away of the joints).

Being FAT also means that the overall quality of life is either compromised or suffers in very measurable ways. I remember being so physically exhausted that a simple task — such as getting up from the couch to get a document from my car — was such an effort that I had to muster every ounce of gumption. I remember when it was physically challenging to go up and down the stairs. I've had obese friends talk about not making the hike to the bathroom in a restaurant to avoid the shame of coming back sweaty. Some of my overweight friends have remained standing at someone's house because couch space and sturdy chairs were all occupied and the only available seating was delicate or antique.

Being FAT in America means living in constant shame. We believe that there is something innately wrong and undeserving in us. In marketing, media and entertainment, fat people are stupid, objects of ridicule and humor, or blatantly derided. If we are experiencing shame, we cannot love ourselves, nor can we allow other people to love us.

Once I realized that food diets would ultimately lead to a weight gain, I began to understand why I couldn't lose weight and keep it off. I had the desire, the motivation, the financial means, the intelligence, the time to spend at the gym, the money to hire a personal trainer, and the will to make myself do the exercises, yet I didn't seem to lose the weight. The breakthrough came when I realized that it had nothing to do with will-power. I have plenty of will-power. I've demonstrated that in many different aspects of my life.

I began to recognize the pattern of wanting very specific foods when I felt different emotions. This was the huge breakthrough. I craved chocolate for the blues, ice cream for loneliness or disappointment, pizza for boredom, coffee with lots of cream when I was tired, and anything crunchy when I felt anxiety.

Once I recognized that most of my hunger was emotional in nature, not a physical need, I also began to understand that stopping this addiction had nothing to do with will-power, desire or drive. I couldn't rationalize my emotions so I began to understand that I couldn't formulate a strategic plan for overcoming this addiction of compulsive overeating. Whatever was driving my overeating transcended my intellectual abilities. This understanding helped me to stop beating myself up for not having enough will-power. I realized that stopping the overeating was not a mental exercise, nor an intellectual decision. This insight took me to a new level.

I, like many Americans, experienced a long-term hideous state of being called "FAT." About five years ago, after years of trying to lose weight with the traditional diet approach, I finally understood that the reason I had gained eighty pounds over a period of ten years was because I had climbed aboard (and fallen off) one diet after another. Each diet met with some level of success. But getting off that diet and going back to my old eating habits contributed to the next three extra pounds, the next five pounds, the next ten pounds. I had always been good about going on a diet and losing fifteen or twenty pounds and sticking to it, even being obsessive while on the diet only to gain all the lost pounds, and gain a few pounds more when I was no longer dedicated to the plan. So

I decided to stop dieting because I finally understood that this was like the Irish adage, "Fool me once, shame on you; fool me twice, thrice, ...twentieth time, shame on me."

But I was caught. I was not happy with my weight and I was ashamed of my body. I knew I didn't want to have my stomach stapled and I didn't want to live on diet pills for the rest of my life. And even when ignoring the side effects of many of these miracle diet pills, they only seem to work for a few weeks. What were my options? I refused to be FAT for the rest of my life. What could I do to end this nightmare?

I was fortunate to realize that there was something out of balance with respect to how much I ate. I gained that insight when I attended Weight Watchers. One of the best things Weight Watchers did for me was to make me face how many calories I ate on an average day. Part of the Weight Watchers regimen involves writing down everything you eat. I realized, "Oh my God, look how much I eat! No wonder I'm so heavy!" So the question evolved: "Why do I eat so much?"

If you are reading this and you are overweight, and you truly don't realize how much you eat, just write it all down. And I mean everything that goes into your mouth, even a stick of gum or a glass of water. After really seeing how much I ate I was then forced to ask the $64 Billion Dollar Question: What makes me eat so much?

I noted that I seldom ate breakfast and survived on coffee (with lots of cream); therefore, I was ravenous at lunch. On most occasions when I went out and enjoyed a four-course dinner — appetizer, salad, entree and dessert — I would still come home and eat. Even after a 4,000-calorie dinner I was STILL hungry. I noticed that the hunger started as I drove home and I began to ponder what I would eat when I arrived. Typically, I began to dream about getting home and making love to Mr. Häagen Dazs and watching a soothing movie. Sometimes the craving was for a plate of nachos blanketed with cheese, sometimes for leftover pizza. Why, after having a wonderful dinner was I still hungry?

One of my friends in undergraduate school, a very bright fellow who went on to complete a Ph.D. program in physics at Princeton, once said that when you generate a question, you have the kernel of the answer. It took the next three years to get answers to my question. I finally realized that I was eating through all of my emotions. I ate when feeling stress, fatigue, disappointment, loneliness... name an emotion and I could name a food that would help me smother it.

So I began to wonder: If I could stop eating through my emotions, would it make a big difference in my life? The answer has been a definite and life-affirming YES! I finally did understand what works and why other attempts didn't really work. This book is a recounting of the journey and a sharing of what actually does profoundly work.

Other people have also recognized many of the instructions, insights, coping lists, and strategies that you will find in this program. Insight is not the sole property of any one human being. The difference is that I finally understood the reason people spend hundreds and thousands of dollars on exercise equipment and never use it. Or the reason people join a health club and only go for the first six weeks while paying for much longer.

The reason we can only stay on a diet for a few months is because there are underlying causes that don't support staying on a program that is foreign to our emotional psyche and our instinct for self-preservation and gratification. Asking someone for whom food is a means of coping with life to stop overeating without providing alternative strategies or coping tools is cruel and finally ineffective.

If you are currently following a diet and it is working, the principles and observations outlined in this book might not appeal to you, or they may augment your current efforts. This work entails accepting and processing our emotions so that we are released from having to be "good" and eat less fat, less meat, fewer carbohydrates, and so on.

The behavioral change is about letting the fire that fuels emotion burn until it is extinguished. We must sit with that fire — enduring emotional discomfort — convinced that it is a worthwhile investment in ourselves. We have experienced the failure of many diets. Until we are willing to admit this reality, any approach to healing emotional eating could not possibly be embraced because the current diet may be working.

Diets work. They all work… but only while there is weight loss, a vision of why we are losing weight and while we are still enthused about our progress. Consequently we have to endorse the diet and reject anything that challenges the diet. The question is: Can you sustain that level of deprivation for the rest of your life? What happens when you go back to eating what is normal for you? What could you live with for the rest of your life?

I have heard of smokers not wanting to give up their cigarettes for fear of gaining weight. I realized that I needed to evolve not beyond one addiction, but beyond whatever it is that causes addictive behavior. My journey began as a search; ending my eating problem was the goal, but as I advanced, I realized that most addictions have many commonalities and the required understanding was to evolve beyond addictive behavior altogether.

I am not going to follow the formula of most books in this genre and give you five or six chapters on the issues that led me to overeating. If you are reading this book, you probably have your own trauma, your list of reasons why you are tired of being FAT, your own drama. You just want to end it. However, I must warn you that this is a book about transformation, not temporary change. We use diets to change, but we only transform when we are willing to rise above the status quo, resist mass marketing and end cycles of dieting.

Overeating, for most overweight people, is the primary coping mechanism that makes our life functional or at least bearable. Above all, humans have amazingly complex survival instincts. Once we had to survive fierce creatures, but the jungle has changed and we now face the foes of stress and emotional isolation. Our coping mechanism has evolved to match our current hostile environment. Not everyone ends up overeating to cope with the demands of the modern jungle. Some people choose cigarettes, some choose liquor, drugs, sex, exercise, power, anorexia or some other form of emotional suppression. Others are very fortunate to evolve beyond mere coping mechanisms and can actually face the challenges of what it means to be human in the modern world and thrive in this environment.

After the failure of so many traditional attempts, I got off the main highway and looked to the Eastern philosophies and ancient wisdom. I then combined those insights with what I had learned with my Western-trained mind and arrived at a discerning understanding that the end of diets is reached when we learn self-love, embrace all of our emotions, and honor the wisdom of our bodies.

1 - **our history**

overweight nation

Studies from the Centers for Disease Control and Prevention (CDC) found that the average body weight of Americans increased considerably during the last decade[2]. The term Body Mass Index (BMI) is commonly used when discussing the obesity epidemic. It is a number what shows body weight adjusted for height and can be calculated with simple math using inches and pounds. For people twenty years of age or older, individual BMI falls into one of four categories: underweight, normal, overweight, or obese.

- Underweight less than 18.5
- Normal weight between 18.5 and 24.9
- Overweight between 25 and 29.9
- Obese over 30

* To calculate your own BMI, go to www.nhlbisupport.com/bmi, or use the formula BMI = ((weight/ height)/height) * 703. Weight is entered in pounds and height in inches. For example, if your weight is 170 lbs, and your height is 5'4", which equals 64", you would calculate (170/64)/64) * 703 which equals a BMI of 29.2.

The percentage of U.S. adults who are obese grew from 12% in 1991 to 29.5% in 2006, a 246% increase. The prevalence of overweight adults also increased from 45% in 1991 to 65.2% in 2006. In 1985, only a few states were participating in the CDC's Behavioral Risk Factor Surveillance System and providing obesity data. In 2001, 20 states had obesity prevalence rates of 15%-19%, 29 states had rates of 20%-24%, and one state reported a rate of more than 25%.

Obesity in the United States has been increasingly cited as a major health issue in recent decades, 2 out 3 Americans are now considered overweight[3]. While many industrialized countries have experienced similar increases, obesity rates in the United States are among the highest in the world. Should current trends continue, 75% of adults in the US are projected to be overweight and 41% obese by 2015. The table on the next page depicts this trend:

1

Overweight and obesity

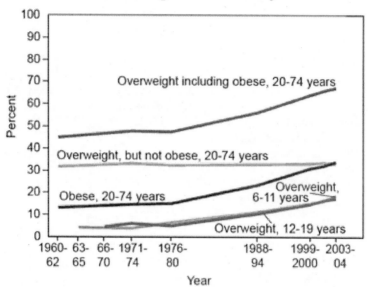

SOURCES: Centers for Disease Control and Prevention. National Center for Health Statistics. Health, United States, 2006. Data from the National Health and Nutritional Health and Nutrition Examination Survey.

On May 14 newspaper reporter Laura Meckler wrote an article for the Associated Press titled Obesity Reported to Cost U.S. $93 Billion a Year. In this article, Meckler explains that obesity related health issues cost the U.S. economy more than tobacco and alcohol related health issues combined. The Internal Revenue Service has recognized obesity as a medical disease. As such, participation in a weight-loss program, when a physician diagnoses obesity, is deductible as a medical expense.

According to Marketdata Enterprises, a Florida research group, about 52 million U.S. dieters fuel a weight-loss market worth $60.92 billion per year. Marketdata predicts that the diet industry will continue its annual growth of about 5.8%, with much of the business coming from baby boomers. It is interesting to compare the weight-gain trend with the growth of the diet industry. Some examples of how the diet industry is segmented and its forecasted growth (in billions of dollars) are depicted in the following table:

chapter 1: our history

Marketdata's income estimates of major segments of the U.S. diet industry[4] (in billions of dollars)

	2002	2003	2004	2005	2008
Diet soft drinks	$14.86	$16.58	$17.08	$18.00	$22.98
Artificial sweeteners	$1.79	$1.99	$2.06	$2.17	$2.77
Health club revenues	$13.10	$14.10	$15.10	$16.30	$19.72
Commercial weight-loss centers	$1.71	$1.71	$1.83	$2.02	$2.60
Low cal/diet foods	$2.40	$2.23	$2.21	$2.37	$2.69
Appetite suppressants	$1.41	$1.11	$1.05	$1.18	$1.51
Bariatric surgery	$1.57	$2.57	$3.50	$2.97	$4.12
Prescription diet drugs	$0.51	$0.43	$0.41	$0.42	$0.72
VLCD/LCD programs	$0.28	$0.31	$0.34	$0.38	$0.50
Diet books/exercise videos	$1.38	$1.47	$1.57	$1.67	$2.01
TOTAL INDUSTRY:	**$39.84**	**$43.68**	**$46.35**	**$48.63**	**$60.96**

Companies that specialize in weight-loss management, such as Weight Watchers™ and Jenny Craig™, anticipate that the current growth rate of 5.8% per year will continue. So the question is: Why are we getting fatter when the diet industry is offering such a wide selection of products?

Although there is no evil plot to keep us fat, there isn't much evidence that the diet industry is having any success in helping Americans lose weight permanently. It is obvious that despite the billions, not millions but BILLIONS, of dollars spent every year in attempts to get thinner, Americans are getting fatter.

we tried dieting, we tried motivation

First, let's define what a diet is. Most diets are regimented, restrictive, short-term guidelines for what to eat, and in some cases when to eat, in order to achieve rapid weight loss. For emotional eaters, i.e. a person who experiences hunger when there is an emotional imbalance, diets don't work. Sure, many of us seem to be able to stick to a diet for weeks and sometimes even months, but sooner or later we go back to our habitual method of coping with life, which is food. For those of us who have struggled for many years and have tried a variety of diets without lasting success, dieting is just a setup for another disappointment. Let me illustrate this point with a real life story.

Dilia De La Altagracia

Like many of us, Jody woke up one day and decided that this was it! She was finished being FAT. She was fed up with not having the life she wanted and deserved. She was going to change her life and do something about those unwanted pounds. Jody began the Weight Watchers™ program. She ate exactly what she was supposed to eat. She measured food, she weighed food, she looked up points for every food, she even downloaded a program to her Palm Pilot™ to help count food points. She convinced all of us to meet her at salad bars instead of our usual high-calorie haunts.

Jody began a modest exercise program. She went to weekly meetings and weighed in. Every week Jody reported a one, two, three or sometimes even six-pound loss. Jody was the Weight Watchers™ poster child. Within eight months, Jody had lost a whopping 80 pounds. She looked fabulous and she felt great. She bought a gorgeous new wardrobe and spent $600 on a beautiful vintage gown that she wore to a fancy Valentine's Day ball. As her weight dropped, her confidence rose; she carried herself as a beautiful woman, and she even began to go out on dates.

We were all envious of our friend Jody, and we seriously considered following her path to thinness. Jody was slim and gorgeous for six months. But having reached her goals, she stopped going to the meetings. After dating proved to be unsatisfying, she stopped writing down every single piece of food she ate. One day Jody was upset with her work and decided to hell with the diet; she was fed up with counting and weighing.

Jody went off the plan and began to eat as she had for a large part of her adult life. She went back to soothing her emotions with food. Within four months, Jody gained not only the 80 pounds she had lost, but an additional 15 pounds.

If you live and breathe and are part of our modern world, you can find thousands of variations of this same story. There are millions of Americans who have lost weight but, after going off the diet, have regained those lost pounds – and then some. Everyone gets tired of diet plans. We want out of restrictive, prison-like routines. We have a bad day, we want something that makes us feel better, and thus ends many a diet. Or we have something to celebrate and we don't know how to feel happy within the constraints of the diet, so out the window goes the diet. Sooner or later, we want to eat what other people seem to be able to eat without becoming FAT.

chapter 1: our history

We have finally realized that most diets don't work, at least not for the long haul. As a matter of fact dieting, or more precisely going off a diet, is the chief reason that people gain weight. Consequently, the phrase "long term weight loss" has crept into our vocabulary. Marketers, ever quick to detect trends, become sophisticated and have adopted this catch phrase to lure us back to their "new" diet program, diet patch, diet pill or to whatever this year's promise of sure-fire weight loss and eternal thinness might be.

After reading the scientific data I finally understood that dieting is the best way to gain weight. Let me restate this in a different manner. If you are a thin person and you want to gain a few pounds, skip the protein drinks and mega calorie meals. The most effective way to lose weight is to temporarily limit your caloric intake and disrupt your natural set point – the weight balance that your body strives to maintain. A restrictive diet sends a message that you are in starvation mode. Your magnificent and intelligent body then adjusts itself to live within the constraints of the available calories and recalibrates itself to a lower set-point. It is widely known that most of us cannot live permanently with the diets we undertake; sooner or later, we go back to our old behavior and voilà, everything we just lost is regained, plus more.

Dieters are like the character in Greek mythology, Sisyphus. He was cursed to roll a large rock uphill, only to have it roll down again as soon as it reached the top. We have become the modern day Sisyphus; we are condemned to experience the joy of watching the numbers on the scale tick down, only to experience profound disappointment as our weight rolls back up once the diet ends.

After I failed at yet another diet, I finally wondered how to get off this infernal roller coaster. Why do I get hungry when I experience the slightest emotional discomfort? What can I do to stop eating my way through emotions?

Examining my friend Jody's success, I wondered how she had dealt with her emotions for all of those months while she was not overeating. What happens during these diet periods when we seem to overcome our emotional eating behavior?

I had experienced two episodes in my life that radically changed my eating habits overnight. The first was when I was pregnant, and the second was when I had an intense, highly charged Internet romance. So

Dilia De La Altagracia

I know from firsthand experience that external motivators do work –
temporarily – in helping us reach our desired weight.

During my pregnancy, the nurse practitioner explained to me the
potential damage to my baby if I consumed coffee or alcohol. After
years of drinking four cups of coffee every morning, my caffeine
craving magically went away. After years of being a social drinker,
there was no struggle in giving up alcohol for a few months if it meant
greater well-being for my son. Why did that miraculous change of
behavior happen?

For three months during my Internet romance I experienced the feeling
of romantic love in all its splendor, poetry and promise. Because I
didn't want this man to meet me while I was fat, I didn't rush into a
face-to-face meeting. Overnight I became conscientious about what I
ate, I exercised religiously, and in three short months I lost 38 pounds.
Unlike pregnancy, when some of my eating behaviors were postponed
by a sense of duty and a protective maternal instinct, this time the elixir
of romance overshadowed the emotional hunger... for a while. It was
extraordinary that even on vacation at a five-star hotel, I could walk
past the most sumptuous buffet and there was no struggle, no need to
negotiate with the food demons. The compulsion to eat was truly and
miraculously gone. Many people report this phenomenon during the
first stages of romantic love, when we are more worried about losing
the gloss from our lips (and the weight from our hips) than any
pleasures from food.

I was fortunate that my Internet romance ended abruptly when I
discovered that my cyber soul mate was already married. What I
learned from that experience was an understanding that something
beyond genetics, childhood issues, or big bones was fueling the
overeating After all, only one thing had changed: I was getting a few
steamy emails every day, and I had a compelling and deadline to be
thin by the time I would meet my Internet Romeo.

There was a common theme to both of these episodes that caused
significant changes in my eating behavior. I was apparently willing,
able, and determined to change my eating habits when there was an
external force motivating the behavioral change. While pregnant, I
found the ability to forgo my coffee and alcohol desires for the well-
being of my son. However this was not a kindness I had ever extended
to myself; I had never changed my eating behavior for my own well-
being. In the case of the Internet fling, I was willing to change my

chapter 1: our history

behavior hoping to win the approval of a man. It was obvious that I'm an externally motivated person because I had never changed eating behavior just for myself. Could I find another spellbinding romance to motivate a change in my eating behaviors? But the questions this time were different. If I understood unconscious eating habits, I had a chance to be thin.

I tried to emulate those external motivators in order to move toward my goals. I tried to create an external reward structure that would generate motivation to help me in the quest for weight loss. I purchased stunning dresses in the size of my ideal body. My sister enticed me with a trip to Italy if I lost an agreed upon number pounds by a specific date. My refrigerator became a collage displaying pictures of role models, snapshots of myself when I was thin, and for extra enticement, photos of some gorgeous Hollywood hunks.

Other people change eating behaviors to lose weight for a wedding, or that special vacation when they want to wear a tiny bikini, or for that fancy ball, or school reunion. Having goals is an important facet of human existence. However, I now know with certainty that these special external motivators yield weight loss only until the fulfillment of the desired event. Once the date passes, there is nothing to short-circuit the emotional hunger, and we go back to established patterns of overeating.

Why do we waddle back to our dysfunctional overeating behavior? We know how pleasant it is to live without the shame of being FAT. We know what we need to do to lose weight. What pulls us, time and time again, to eating habits that lead to self-hatred?

When I finally stopped looking for external motivations, I found the way to lose weight permanently. I admitted to myself that I was dealing with an addiction, and that I had to begin looking inside for the causes of that addiction, not to external motivation. I realized that by continuing on my current path I was in essence exchanging one addiction for another: food for co-dependency, or in the case of the ex-smoker who gains weight, cigarettes for food. Until I owned my addiction emotionally – and was even willing to use the word "addiction" – I could do nothing to end it. The correlation between my emotions and overeating became clearer. This allowed me to take responsibility for my addiction and finally opened the door to a comprehensive solution.

Dilia De La Altagracia

Even when we know that the miracle short-term diets are too good to be true, we still fall for them. We are so desperate that we will try anything, anything, even if we suspect a con artist is swindling us, in the hope of stopping the misery of being FAT. Studies indicate more than 96% of the people who lose weight using a diet gain all the weight back – and more – within months of going off the diet. And it doesn't matter what type of diet: low fat, high protein, no carbohydrates, more vegetables, or just fewer calories.

A reasonable question to ask is why we don't simply stay, for the rest of our lives, in the program that got us to our weight goals. After all, that is a small price to pay not to be FAT. While this is a reasonable question, the reality is that willpower and external motivators do not last a lifetime. They counteract the overeating behavior until we reach our external goal and get to wear that bikini on the beach, or we experience ourselves at the weight that we had hoped would change our lives. When the vacation has been taken, or the wedding is over, there is nothing to counteract the emotional needs that manifest as hunger. When we arrive at our goal weight, if we don't get deeper satisfaction than the short-term goal can provide, we go back to the behavior that we know and that temporarily makes us feel better.

Having willpower and dreams is admirable, but we cannot deny our emotions for the rest of our lives. The truth is that many of us have issues that need to be addressed. Some of us have profound problems stemming from childhood. Some of us have serious self-esteem issues. Some of us can't even say self-love, let alone experience it. We have not learned to deal effectively with many of our emotions. Food is the only thing we know that seems to make us stop feeling bad.

We are sometimes able to stay focused for months because we truly believe that when we become thin, life will be better. When I reached my goal weight and began to re-experience life without the stigma of being FAT, the dreams I had about being thin did not come true. After all of those months of disciplined work, I went back to the one thing that mitigated the loneliness, the frustration of my family interactions, the sadness of working at an unfulfilling job, the one thing that seemed to help me deal with my emotions. I went back to binge eating.

It is obvious that for all the people who do achieve lifelong weight loss, the key is a profound, life-altering, behavioral change that brings about a new relationship with food. The breakthrough is not the diets; it is in understanding the function of the overeating behavior and developing healthy life skills to be with our emotions. But that epiphany occurs for less than three percent of people who go on diets. Unfortunately, what gets publicized is the success of the diet, the fad, the gimmick, not the underlying emotional growth that led to the lifelong changes.

We have to deal with the factors that trigger our hunger. Until we develop meaningful ways of being with our emotions and with the reality of the ups and downs of human existence, no diet in the world is going to help us become lean and fit for the rest of our lives. Sooner or later we will go back to food because we still need the emotional fix.

Real change will occur when we feel the emotions that fuel hunger. Diets will work while our enthusiasm, hope, and desires short-circuit the over-eating behavior and keep our feelings at bay. But the suppressed emotions will overwhelm that enthusiasm. Gradually we let down our guard, or something upsetting happens, and because we've not developed any other means to deal with these emotions, we resort to food and overeating. Until we have an effective means of dealing with our emotional hunger, all dieting attempts will be short-lived, and with each diet failure our self-esteem erodes further.

When I finally learned that losing weight is a long journey and not a quick fix, I began not only to lose weight but also to make meaningful and profound changes in my life. When I understood that eating twenty pounds of frustration, thirty pounds of loneliness, twenty-five pounds of anger, or thirty-five pounds of disappointment was not in my best interest, I began to ask myself how I could effectively cope with these emotions instead of munching my way through them. Only then was I able to eat consciously for the long term. As the Zen saying goes, "When the student is ready, the teacher will appear."

will power, intelligence and facts, oh my!

I used to value intelligence above all other human qualities. Consequently, when the time came to address the problem of being overweight, I naturally focused my energies on what I needed to understand about calories, exercise, behavioral patterns, food mixing, diet pills, and so on. Every specialist I consulted had a theory. Psychiatrists gave me the chemical imbalance theory, medical doctors cited calories, geneticists talked about fat genes, and exercise gurus denounced couch potatoes. When you have a hammer, everything looks like a nail.

Like all dieters, I knew of people who had lost weight with medical programs or by buying a specific piece of equipment; others lost it when they started taking the newest diet pill. And they all knew how to gain it back after the program ended, or they got bored with exercises, or the effect of the diet pill wore off. Research indicates that there are people who do in fact have a chemical deficiency or brain imbalance and are successfully helped by lithium or other chemical therapies. However, the percentage of people for whom weight is a physiological issue is so negligible that without compelling evidence, anyone who pursues that road is in for a rude awakening, not to mention substantial expense. It was in my best interest to run away from fantasies and face the reality of my addiction to food and my misplaced faith in quick-fix solutions.

Traditional weight-loss wisdom has told us that we need to get some information and training about what foods to avoid, what foods to eat and when to eat them, that we have to exercise, that we must stop eating four hours before going to bed, drink eight glasses of water daily, and so on. We just have to get the facts; we have to find that magical piece of data that will set us free. This quest has taken us through no-fat diets, no-carbohydrate diets, high-protein diets, the Atkins Diet™, the Pritikin Diet™, and countless others, as well as numerous exercise regimens. The list goes on and on. These approaches all have testimonials from people who appear to be living proof that their respective systems work. Like me, you may have tried many, if not all of them.

Once we saw that traditional wisdom didn't work for us we migrated from diet or exercise programs to the behavior-based solution. The message was consistent and repetitive: People who are successful in maintaining their weight invoke personal restraint and willpower. All you need is willpower. The fallacy was in trying to emulate those for whom food is not a means of dealing with their emotions. Their hunger is not fueled by the same motivations experienced by emotional eaters.

Haven't you ever been told by a thin person, "Just eat this or that. Just burn more calories than you consume. Just have your last meal by 7:30 P.M. Just exercise four times a week. Just stop eating." But for emotional eaters, food is as reassuring as a lullaby, as calming as gentle rain, as relaxing as a luscious bubble bath, as entertaining as a good movie. There is something in us that finds the same qualities in food that non-emotional eaters find in other healing and self-sustaining alternatives. We have learned that food helps us deal with difficulties

chapter 1: our history

and pain in our lives, and if food is how we deal with our emotions, why would anyone advise us to stop eating? It's like asking a human to stop consuming oxygen. Food is our default coping mechanism. The reality is that non-emotional eaters have alternative means of dealing with their emotions and often they don't understand that food is how we deal with ours. I could not stop overeating by an act of will. I tried for many years.

Pursuing willpower and personal self-restraint once again led me to a sense of inadequacy. An important part of the work we must do is to understand that having an intellectual appreciation of anything doesn't change behavior. Let me give you an example. Several years ago I had a romantic crush. I intellectually understood that he was not the right man for me, that I needed to give up the emotional attachment. I found that my intellectual resolution would last for only a few days and then I would find myself longing to be with him. I overcame the obsession only when I was finally able to emotionally experience the truth of what I had understood intellectually; that he was not the right man for me.

This taught me a very important lesson. Intellectualizing and rationalizing do nothing for our emotional attachments. Once we relieve our emotional discomfort with food, once we are emotionally wedded to anything, we can temporarily ignore the deeper need, but it will always create an emotional undertow. Remember how many times you've been good and tried to ignore the food you were craving. Remember how many times you promised yourself that this time was it, this time you were really going to stick to that diet and reach your ideal weight. This lesson is one of the keys to overcoming eating that is triggered by emotional needs.

I am not minimizing the value of knowledge. I spent 18 years being trained to memorize facts, reason things out, develop theorems, and use logic, so many of my skills are mental in nature. I was taught that my mind controls my body. I know the power of knowledge and reason, and I know that it is helpful in the beginning to understand intellectually how to deal with emotional upset instead of running to the refrigerator. In truth understanding drives another nail into the coffin of inadequacy, because now we know better, but understanding alone is insufficient. It is critical to know that willpower, intelligence, facts and figures, good intentions, and knowing better do little to help us stop overeating. Do you really believe that fat people don't have any willpower? Do you really believe fat people don't know that if they eat less they will lose weight? Do you really believe people don't know that exercising, drinking more water, and not eating late is healthful? Do you really believe that lack of information keeps us FAT or that most people are overweight because they don't know how to lose weight? To the contrary, we are experts at losing weight. It is not a matter of better data or more information. The End of Diets is about having access to our emotions. It is only when we relieve emotional stress that overeating ceases to be a driving force.

Once we truly understand that dieting without addressing the underlying emotions that fuel hunger is merely a short-term solution, we can make lifelong changes. Otherwise we are doomed to be tantalized by this year's new fad for the rest of our lives. We release emotional attachment only by emotional cleansing. Those of us who value intelligence above all else will continue to search for a solution consistent with processes of the mind. Emotional hunger cannot be rationalized. It cannot be talked down, it cannot be reasoned against. It can be short-circuited for periods of time, but it cannot be wished away.

what is emotional hunger?

Emotional hunger is the false belief that food makes us feel better. It is longing for food whenever there is any discomfort in our emotional state. Emotional hunger is using food to satisfy needs that are not being fulfilled in other ways. It is being more attuned to how food will make us feel than to our emotions. Though the fix is temporary, we have learned that food will alleviate loneliness, boredom, shame, depression, and on and on.

Emotional hunger equates celebration with food. For many of us it is the way that we know to express love – the hard work of cooking a grand meal and sharing from the heart. It is being able to connect with people only when we are all eating.

Emotional hunger is getting up in the middle of the night and bargaining with the demons of physical hunger. How many times did I awake in the middle of the night knowing that the only way to sleep was to stuff myself so the work of digestion would make me drowsy?

Emotional hunger means lacking the ability to choose healthy options for our sustenance. It is being totally oblivious to how many calories we are actually consuming in one day. It is having the attitude of

chapter 1: our history

"Frankly, Scarlet, I don't give a damn," I need to get this report done or deal with the issues or just feel better right now, and food is what allows me to function. Emotional hunger is being mesmerized by a little piece of bread left on the plate. Emotional hunger is salivating over every small morsel of food before we taste it. It is feeling comforted by food. It is getting overexcited at the aroma and taste of pizza. It is feeling satiated only after the stomach has gone past its physical limit. It is believing that we will feel better if we have an extra piece of cheesecake. It is dealing with the ups and downs of life with food.

Food is the celebration. It is taking a break from work by eating. It is measuring the traumas of life by what is being consumed. It is driving home after a five-course gourmet dinner and thinking "What am I going to eat when I get home?" Emotional hunger is knowing that Mr. Häagen Dazs™ is going to make me feel sooo good, so comforted Saturday night when I stay in and watch my favorite movie.

Emotional eating, like all addictions, has strong compulsive elements. It is not being able to chew fast enough, inhaling food, unable to breathe when food is in our mouths – like sharks in a frenzy or a heroin addict getting a fix. It means desperate measures and an overwhelming sense of urgency that we MUST HAVE FOOD RIGHT NOW. Emotional eating drives and compels us like locusts devouring crops: It cannot be reasoned with or calmed.

There are patterns of highs and lows in the life of every addict. Emotional hunger is about being addicted to the roller-coaster ride; the high of the binge and the low of the self-hate. "Why did I overeat again? I know better." What do you mean, "I'm addicted to the self-hate"? How can I possibly want the degrading feeling of being FAT? Most of us understand the pleasure of the food. But many of us find it difficult to comprehend that emotional eating also provides the opportunity for self-loathing, and therefore, at some psychic level we must need these feelings in our lives. To finally give up my addictive overeating behavior, I had to give up the constant search for the highs that the binge momentarily gave me. Only then would I stop experiencing the lows of self-hatred.

Even when one becomes aware of these destructive behaviors, emotional eating doesn't stop. As stated previously neither intellectualization, information, nor desperation can stop emotional eating. The intellect is weak in comparison to our emotional drive.

13

Once we want something emotionally, no amount of reason will talk us out of it. Why do you think we say "Love is blind"? Why should you stop eating if food is what seems to create an emotional balance to our lives? How could you stop eating if food makes your life bearable and functional?

Being conscious of our emotions stops emotional eating. In the next chapters we will embark on a journey to leave behind the insidious compulsion of emotional eating once and for all. The journey will teach us to sensitize ourselves to the mechanisms that lead to emotional eating, help us become aware of our emotions, and most importantly, teach us to experience our emotions so we can stop eating through them.

2 - **preparing for the journey**

i've had it, i'm tired

The journey toward healing the emotional hunger began by verbalizing my feelings about being FAT. As the list grew, the statements changed from business-like assessments to outpourings of anger, shame and frustration. Some examples of these statements are:

- I'm missing many experiences in my life because of how I feel about myself.
- The quality of my life is jeopardized because I'm overweight.
- My options for activities are limited by my weight.
- I'm eating my emotions.
- I'm out of touch with my emotions.
- I'm sick of being FAT.
- I don't want to be ashamed of myself any longer.
- I'm so disgusted with my weight; I can't stand hearing myself complain about it anymore.

These statements began as observations, but until I failed, again and again and yet again and got tired of being conned by yet another miracle diet, I didn't consider addressing the weight losing business from a fundamental and comprehensive approach. Because I'd been taught that it was a matter of finding the right food combination, I didn't ask what else I could do. Until I lived these statements and felt the pain brutally, I was not willing to look into the healing that involved dealing with my emotions. Until the student is ready, the teacher does not appear.

getting beyond denial

Our human psyche has an amazing capacity to protect us from melting down in the face of overwhelming or devastating situations. If you've read psychological literature, you understand what happens when we are presented with data we cannot accept all at once, for example the death of a child or a spouse. The first stage of grief is denial.

For many of us who have experienced the death of a loved one, the grief is truly devastating. I remember the evening my father died

Dilia De La Altagracia

unexpectedly at the age of 43 when I was 17 years old. At the beginning, all I wanted to do was take care of logistics: I had to visit the morgue to identify his body, make funeral arrangements, return his car to the house, etc. But when I was finally alone and had to face his death, I could no longer avoid the depth of my sadness. My grief went from choking tears to a sensation of intense physical burning that I can only describe as having my internal organs doused in gasoline and set on fire.

Sometimes we are just not ready; we need more time to face the pain. We are not emotionally ready to confront it. Pure grief is not an emotion any rational human being would want to face without first bargaining with the devil himself. So you see denial, or better stated postponement, is a healthy and necessary reaction.

Denial becomes an unhealthy pattern if we consistently avoid pain and make denial a lifestyle, if we are unwilling to even think of experiencing any pain. I remember eight years ago attempting to read Geneen Roth's book *Feeding the Hungry Heart* and literally putting it down because I couldn't cope with my overwhelming pain as I read the stories of women who were facing the same eating addiction. At that time I was not willing to experience my own pain. I was reading to gain insight and understanding, not to learn about myself or change my behavior.

Most of us have evolved intricate self-preservation mechanisms that keep us from having to deal with intolerable emotions until we feel safe and ready. When I began to ask, "How do I effectively deal with my loneliness? How else can I handle all this emotion besides eating through it?" I had to ask, "Can I be with my loneliness and feel it?" The answer was a barely audible, "No," and a continuation of the binge rituals.

I attempted to read books like *Feeding the Hungry Heart* when I had not achieved the emotional maturity to be with myself. I still believed that there was a diet to deal with my weight issue: I was still in search of the magic pill. More importantly I did not have the courage to embark on the necessary journey within. Until we have tools other than a microwave and a fork to deal with emotions, until we begin to ask for help and trust that the help will be there when we call on it, and until we know that sitting with these emotions will not shatter us, we will continue to live in denial.

chapter 2: preparing for the journey

Although denial is an inevitable stage on the road to recovery, we need to evolve beyond it to reach acceptance. Sometimes that evolution is aided by supportive friends, psychotherapy, or controlled environments. If, as you begin this book, you find that you are experiencing too much anxiety or emotional discomfort, you will put the book down. That is human; that is your self-preservation system at work. You might subconsciously say "the hell with this" and pursue the next miracle diet, the next easy promise of thinness, or you might ask yourself: "Do I need help here? Can I do this all by myself?"

Practically speaking, if you started with the intention that this time you really are going to lose weight and you stop halfway through this book, outside help is probably in order. This is transformational work, not the next diet. If you have any doubt whether or not you should be doing this work by yourself, get help. Friends or professionals can assist you in crossing the bridge from denial to acceptance.

While I strongly advocate support, I also want to caution against blowing experiences out of proportion. Don't make a soap opera of your journey by getting caught up in the "Melodrama of Me." The journey might be difficult and necessitate learning life skills that you don't currently have but over-dramatizing doesn't serve you nor will it help you lose weight.

As you gain access to new tools and become willing to face your pain, you will eventually be convinced that you are done with the false promises of fad diets. For most of us, this happens only after we hit bottom. Alcoholics describe this as "waking up in the gutter." When we have failed at every diet, when we have touched the wound itself, when we have had enough, this is when the door to emotional maturity opens.

self-love: the power to heal emotional hunger

I kept asking myself why did I have this self-defeating overeating behavior. I had the intelligence to run multimillion dollar projects, so why did I lack the intelligence to stop eating? I had all the qualities of a good mother, so why could I not extend these same kindnesses toward myself and regulate what I ate? I was a good friend and knew how to nurture and love my companions, so why could I not be a kind and supportive essence to myself? Why couldn't I love myself enough to stop this insidious behavior?

Dilia De La Altagracia

I remember singing "The Greatest Love of All," and for the life of me, I really didn't get the line, "Learning to love yourself is the greatest love of all." What is self-love? What does it look like? What does it feel like? Why is it important in the quest to stop emotional eating?

I finally realized that I was afraid of something unknown, primordial, and contrary to the messages I had received in my formative years, so when I read the following quote I began to question the origin of my fear about self-love:

> Our deepest fear is not that we are inadequate.
> Our deepest fear is that we are powerful beyond measure.
> It is our light, not our darkness that most frightens us.
> We ask ourselves, who am I to be brilliant,
> gorgeous, talented and fabulous?
>
> Actually, who are you not to be?
> You are a child of God.
> Your playing small doesn't serve the world.
> There's nothing enlightened about shrinking
> so that other people won't feel insecure around you.
> We were born to make manifest the glory of God that is within us.
> It's not just in some of us; it's in everyone.
>
> And as we let our own light shine,
> we unconsciously give other people permission to do the same.
> As we are liberated from our own fear,
> our presence automatically liberates others.
>
> – Marianne Williamson

I began my personal journey in search of a woman who loved herself. I began asking questions about why I have so much difficulty accepting the concept of self-love. I had been much better at sacrificing myself than at discovering and honoring my own passion. Who am I? What truly makes me happy? What makes me vital? Initially I had to revisit the times and places where I first learned the definition of self-love.

For me, the concept of self-love had always been cross-wired with vanity, narcissism, and selfishness. It seemed contradictory that self-love would help in my quest to lose weight. If I had any chance of learning self-love, I needed to explore the origins of my beliefs about self-love. I had to learn the distinction between self-love and those less

18

chapter 2: preparing for the journey

desirable traits. I had to revisit all the messages I had received as a child:

- Share with your brother – don't be selfish.
- Selfishness is the greatest curse of the human race.
- Vanity, thy name is woman.
- Love is what is left in a relationship after selfishness is taken out.

As I examined these messages I began to understand the source of my difficulties in accepting the concept of self-love. Let's examine the distinctions between vanity, narcissism and selfishness so we can understand how they differ from self-love.

vanity

Vanity is the belief that we deserve love on the basis of how well we fulfill popular ideals. For example, we believe that we should be loved because we are exceptionally intelligent or beautiful. Vanity is not self-love; it is based on conditions (e.g., our supposed fulfillment of an ideal). In contrast, love is unconditional.

Ideals are unattainable by humans. Thus, to believe that we have attained an ideal on which we can base our vanity, we must repress our awareness of the occasions when we do not attain the ideal. For example, someone who is vain might deny or hate the pimple on an otherwise beautiful face. When we hate or deny any aspect of ourselves, we do not love ourselves.

narcissism

Narcissism is an obsession with oneself to the exclusion of other people. Narcissism is not self-love because it ignores the aspects of our humanity that are fulfilled through interaction with other people. There is a type of nourishment that comes to us only from ourselves. But narcissism is mere infatuation; it does not nourish so we spend an inordinate amount of time focused on ourselves in a futile attempt to be satisfied. In contrast, if we experience self-love, we achieve satisfaction, and then we can turn our attention to other aspects of our lives (including other people).

Dilia De La Altagracia

selfishness

Selfishness is based on egotism and is synonymous with greed. It's having your mind on yourself all the time: my time, my happiness, my friends, my family, my job, my clothes, my looks, my money, and my stuff! Because I believed that the opposite of generosity was greed, I tended to be overly generous and repressed the discernment that not all occasions and all people deserved my generosity. In contrast, I found that true self-love is about trusting our judgment, accepting who we are, looking out for our best interests, and setting our needs as a priority.

I had difficulty embracing the concept of self-love because I had defined it incorrectly. At the core self-love means allowing ourselves to be transformed by the power of the love that is already within us, a love that we already know how to give others, a love that needs to work at home first. The first step in healing my overeating addiction was to trust that loving myself was critical in stopping a destructive behavior that I did not want in my life.

As I began to explore the concept of self-love, I found that it was important to first cultivate the qualities that ultimately culminate in self-love – only then can we experience love that is lived rather than love that is merely understood. This experience leads to self-esteem and self-confidence.

   • Self-esteem enables us to adopt a lenient attitude toward our shortcomings without being complacent about them. It allows us to think highly of ourselves without overlooking our humanity.

   • Self-confidence helps to convince us we can succeed when we are being put to the test. This involves the ability to act. Failure to adopt a confident attitude means being haunted by self-deprecation, constantly doubting ourselves and undermining our right to be assertive and happy.

   • Self-love belongs to the realm of "being." It means trusting our judgment and accepting all our emotions. It is the practical manifestation of love for ourselves.

Loving ourselves is based on learning about ourselves, and that involves embarking on a path of self-discovery. We must learn our likes and dislikes. We must learn what gives us vitality and a sense of

chapter 2: preparing for the journey

fulfillment, what makes us happy, what we can do for hours that energizes us. Who are the people that truly nourish us? When do we feel good about ourselves? When are we at our best? What are the activities that drain and debilitate us? What are the activities that make us feel refreshed and alive?

Self-love feels good. Pleasure and happiness are our birthrights – experiencing the flow of spiritual life. As we love ourselves, that life force stirs within us a wealth of new energy and a new ability to take care of ourselves much the same way we take care of those we love. Moving from understanding to manifestation and taking action in our best interest is where true self-love resides, and when we can do that, we stop overeating.

Our make-up is diverse and complex. We are physical, emotional, intellectual and spiritual beings, with myriad possibilities and needs. Consequently, we must care for our physical manifestation, our emotional balance, our intellectual development, and our spiritual needs. We will examine the actions that lead self-love from these four fundamental human attributes: our physical bodies, our emotional framework, our intellectual makeup and our spiritual essence. What is important are not the concepts but how we incorporate them into our lives. True self-love is not an abstraction, or lofty idea of "How do I love thee? Let me count the ways." It is the daily manifestation of healthy choices that celebrate, support, and embody who we truly are. These daily manifestations let us know that we are experiencing self-love.

physical care

When I think of the beauty, range, and capacities of the body, I am staggered. Have you felt the sensuality expressed by a ballet dancer? Agility expressed by an acrobat? Flow expressed by a gymnast? Strength expressed by a sumo wrestler? Healing power expressed by the touch of a mother? Vibrancy expressed by a Latin dancer? Compassion expressed in healing touch? The beauty expressed by painters and musicians? I am in awe of who we are as human beings. Unquestionably our physical manifestation is, as Shakespeare once stated, "What a piece of work is man! How infinite in faculties!" But as all wise entities, the body needs nourishment and maintenance. We must care for our physical manifestation. Let us first examine how self-love manifests itself in the care of our physical bodies.

Self-acceptance

• We accept and celebrate our unique bodies, even when they don't meet the standards of the advertising industry.

• We celebrate our bodies as wise and magnificent.

• We recognize and acknowledge ourselves as we progress toward flexibility, aerobic capacity, tonality, physical wellness, and healthy weight.

• We understand that most of our negative body judgments arise from our acceptance of other people's opinions, and we must place more value in our own internal wisdom than in others' ideas of what we should look like.

Setting our priorities

• We acknowledge that only when we take care of our physical needs first can we truly take care of others.

• We arrange our schedules to first and foremost ensure that we are meeting our physical needs.

• We take responsibility for our physical needs to stretch, exercise, to rest, to hold and be held, to move joyfully.

• We overcome the erroneous belief that self-love equals selfishness.

• As we grow in vibrancy and self-love we are able to love others genuinely.

We honor that we are worth nurturing

• We understand that the best gift we can give the world is taking care of our physical selves because the world needs more people who are vibrant and energized.

Loving our bodies and seeing their good qualities

• Our bodies are amazing universes that give us pleasure, comfort, movement, physical sensation and awareness.

• We are grateful that despite past overeating and neglectful behavior, for many of us our bodies have always been there for us as healthy, vital, supportive friends.

Rewarding, but also constructively criticizing ourselves

• We value and celebrate our physical selves, our progress, our desire to improve, our longing to be the best that we can be.

chapter 2: preparing for the journey

Nourishing ourselves with good food
• We long for the sense of vitality and well-being in our lives, and consequently we enjoy eating healthy foods.
• We enjoy nurturing ourselves physically.
• We treasure our vitality and enjoy taking care of ourselves.

Becoming our own approving inner parent
• We understand that our opinions and acceptance of our physical bodies influence the quality of our lives.

Turning our negative thoughts into positive affirmations
• Whenever we hear any self-loathing voices about what is wrong with our stomach, thigh, butt, breast, or any other part of our bodies, we affirm our unique physique. We celebrate the wisdom of our bodies.

Giving ourselves what we want and feeling good about it
Part of the self-discovery process is knowing what makes us happy, what brings us joy, what makes us feel vital. Joy comes in many forms. We might derive joy from artistic or creative self-expression, being with those that we love; or engaging in physical activities. The point is to know what really makes us joyous, vital, and exuberant. The following is my list. Please use it as an example and write your own.

• I love feeling light and unencumbered.
• I love the sensuality of a bubble bath.
• I love the aphrodisiac of gourmet food.
• I love dancing and the exhilaration of how the music moves me.
• I love the healing power of a deep-tissue massage.
• I love the textures of life, from silk to a smooth wood sculpture, to fluffy pillows, to the softness of a baby's skin.
• I love snuggling in a warm, clean bed.
• I love wearing beautiful clothes.

emotional balance

Human beings experience a spectrum of emotions and feelings: love, grief, joy, anger, fear, desire, disappointment, to name a few. Balance is the key. We strive to achieve an emotional balance while honoring our emotional needs. Self-love means allowing the experience and expression of these emotions, honoring and accepting our feelings,

23

independent of whether we label them good and bad. How do we manifest emotional balance?

Having self-acceptance
• We embrace all our emotions, even the socially unacceptable ones, which in some cases we have erroneously learned we should never express, e.g., anger.
• We are comfortable with our humanity, our shortcomings, our gifts, our challenges.
• We celebrate our spirituality and uniqueness and talk to ourselves with compassion and forgiveness.
• We express gratitude for all of our blessings.
• We joyfully accept that we are worthy of love because of who we are, not because of what we do or how we look.

Having the ability to say no and set personal boundaries
• We say no to demands that interfere with our personal plans.
• We refuse to forfeit the time we have set aside for fun.
• We say no to events at which the main activity is overeating.
• We provide ourselves the time to experience all of our emotions.
• We accept our emotional need for private time.
• We do not compromise the quality of our lives in the name of family relationships, commitments, friendships, or our jobs.
• We do not ease our emotional pain by eating.

Being worthy of help
• We trust that anyone who helps us experiences the same joy in caring and giving that we do when we extend our help to others.
• We understand and accept – not as personal rejection, but as reality – when others cannot accommodate our request for help.

Being our best friend
• We act as our own best advocate, counselor, and support.
• We learn how to welcome our feelings and how to be with our pain, as we would for a friend.
• We eradicate defeating self-talk and stop comparing our unique being with others.

chapter 2: preparing for the journey

Developing capacity for joy and creativity
• We are responsible for nurturing our creativity, for where there is creativity there is joy, purpose, and growth that truly feeds us.
• We seek out and invest time in activities that contribute to our growth and that make us feel creative, joyful, vital, and purposeful.
• We value the importance of laughter, joy and levity and make time to have fun. These emotions bring relaxation, healing and balance to our lives, and we celebrate their manifestation.
• We embrace our humanity, the challenges and demands of daily life and laugh at ourselves as many times as the opportunity presents itself.

Creating a support system for ourselves
• We choose friends who are willing to tell us when we are blowing things out of proportion or when we are not being compassionate toward ourselves.
• We choose friends who we can hold and who will hold us.
• We radiate energies that reflect our values and attract people who resonate with our essence.
• We take responsibility for the quality of our relationships.
• We are in touch with our emotional needs and are committed to maintaining a healthy emotional balance. Part of this commitment might mean forfeiting activities, forsaking friends or family members that do not contribute to a healthy emotional balance.
• We honor ourselves by not wasting time or money on things that detract from our emotional balance such as mindless TV, degrading magazines, and negative or closed-minded people.

Rewarding, but also constructively criticizing ourselves
• We value and celebrate ourselves, our accomplishments, our uniqueness, and our gifts.
• We accept ourselves as human with all our strengths and weaknesses, positive attributes and imperfections.
• We apologize if we have offended or hurt another human being.
• We rectify our mistakes.
• We seek, then embrace, the lessons that have been given to us through our mistakes.

Owning our ideas

• We own our brilliant ideas and are emotionally proud and satisfied by our accomplishments.
• We are able to laugh at our fallacies, our mistakes by accepting our humanity.

Taking credit for what we accomplish

• We embrace our need to be recognized for our accomplishments.

Trusting ourselves

• We trust our intuition, feelings, guidance, hunches and premonitions.
• We trust our intelligence, reasoning and judgment.
• We trust that our pain is a signal to help us discover what is out of balance.

Becoming our own approving inner parent

• We have an approving inner voice that supports and nurtures our growth, comforts our failures, and helps us maintain a healthy self-esteem.
• We embrace and acknowledge all our unique gifts.

Expressing Gratitude

• We take time to enumerate and offer thanks for the abundant blessings that come to us each day.

Honoring all emotions that cause overeating

• We honor and accept all our emotions, even those that we were taught that we should never express.
• We are grateful when we learn which emotions cause us to overeat.
• We learn to be with all our emotions.
• We embrace the reality that honoring our emotions and learning to be with them allows us to grow as human beings.

Letting ourselves succeed

• Whenever we want to overeat, we take it as a sign that there is an emotional imbalance needing attention. We pause and look inside.

- We uphold the truth that we are meant to live with health, joy, and vitality.
- We maintain our vision even when the map is not complete or we lack some of the life skills to achieve this birthright.
- We accept support when we need it.
- We understand our shortcomings, our gifts, and our challenges as part of the human experience.
- We accept that even this addiction is a door that lead to self-growth.

Giving ourselves what we want and feeling good about it

Part of the self-discovery process is learning why and how we achieve emotional balance. What makes us happy, when do we feel joyous, what makes us laugh, when do we feel loved, or comforted, or understood? The following is my list; please use it as a model to generate your own.

- I feel safe and comforted sharing evenings with friends and family.
- I love playing games with friends.
- I love a day of varied activities.
- I love being moved by human kindness.
- I am proud to see my son growing emotionally and developing into a kind man.
- I am proud of myself and my growth as a human being.
- I am happy that I finally accept and celebrate my uniqueness.
- I am pleased that I accept my mistakes and my growth as part of the human experience.

intellectual growth

We have intellectual needs; our minds need expansion, stimulation and development. We experience self-love when we honor the opportunity that meets our intellectual needs. We experience self-love when we leverage our god-given intelligence to ensure that our emotional, physical and spiritual needs are also met in a world full of choices and multiple demands. How do we manifest intellectual development?

Having self-acceptance
- We understand our shortcomings, our gifts, and our challenges as part of the human experience.
- We understand that even this overeating addiction is a door that will lead us to self-growth.
- We understand our personal needs.

• We appreciate any intellectual stimulation our work might provide.
• We do not compromise the quality of our lives in the name of relationships, commitments, or friendships.
• We understand that caring for others and caring for ourselves is a balancing act, and that sometimes we will not meet everyone's expectations.

Having the ability to say no
• We honor our intellectual choices and say "no" to requests or demands that undermine our intellectual growth.
• We clearly say "no" to work situations that do not honor or develop our intellectual ability.

Setting our priorities first
• We arrange our schedules to ensure that we are developing our intellectual abilities.

Being our best friend
• We acknowledge that only when we are friendly to ourselves can we be a friend to others.

We honor that we are worth nurturing
• We honor the basic human need to keep growing intellectually.

Developing relationships that help us develop our potential
• We are responsible for creating and nurturing relationships that are intellectually stimulating.

Creating a support system for ourselves
• We leverage our intellectual ability by setting up a network of friends, professionals and family that supports and nurtures our intellectual needs.

Constructively criticizing ourselves
• We use our intellectual ability to look at ourselves as objectively as possible.

chapter 2: preparing for the journey

- We understand ourselves as imperfect humans.
- We accept our mistakes and embrace them as an opportunity to learn and evolve.
- We rectify our mistakes.
- We seek, then embrace, the lessons given to us by our mistakes.

Owning our ideas
- We accept the validity of our ideas.

Taking credit for what we accomplish
- We deserve to be recognized for our intellectual accomplishments.

Nourishing ourselves with good ideas
- We enjoy nurturing ourselves intellectually.

Avoiding comparison
- We understand that comparing our intellectual abilities to others is self-defeating and counterproductive.

Trusting ourselves
- We trust our intelligence as we accept our human fallibility.

Authority over ourselves
- We take responsibility for the overall quality of our lives.
- We refuse to let others think on our behalf.

Becoming our own approving inner parents
- We celebrate our intellectual achievement and support the tasks and activities that help us develop our intellectual abilities.

Turning our negative thoughts into positive affirmations
- We understand that we can negate debilitating messages about our intellectual abilities that we receive from the mass media and the world at large. Every time we hear those internal negative voices, those old, self-abusing judgments regarding any intellectual deficiencies, we

acknowledge them as a clue that we need to rewrite our negative programming.

Letting ourselves succeed
• We finish what we start.
• We aren't deterred by setbacks, and we understand that any human endeavor is a process. We accept imperfection.
• We make progress at our own best pace.

Giving ourselves what we want and feeling good about it
Part of the self-discovery process is learning what makes us intellectually curious, engaged, and challenged. The point is to recognize when we are intellectually stimulated. The following is my list; please use it as an example and generate your own.
• I enjoy mentally stimulating games such as Japanese Gõ, Chess, Trivial Pursuit, Jeopardy!
• I enjoy reading exquisite literature.
• I enjoy discovering the insight in poems.
• I enjoy learning in general, but especially about ancient civilizations.
• I enjoy situations and people that are intellectually stimulating and help me grow intellectually.

care of the soul

It has been said that we are spiritual beings having a human experience. Some believe that we are here to learn very specific lessons and to evolve into a higher consciousness. Some state it as becoming more Christ-like, others as learning how to give up suffering. Regardless of your belief, what is important is to honor your spiritual development and feed your soul. How do we manifest the self-love that allows us to care for our souls?

Having self-acceptance
• We embrace our divine nature.
• We accept that even this overeating addiction is a door that will lead us to evolve as spiritual beings.

Having the ability to set boundaries
• We accept our spiritual needs even when they are different from the needs of those we love.

chapter 2: preparing for the journey

Being worthy of love
• We embrace our divinity and uniqueness.
• We emanate joyfully the knowledge that we are worthy of love because of our spiritual nature.

We are worth nurturing
• We honor the importance of taking care of our souls.
• We honor our unfolding spirit. We believe that what the world needs is people who have come alive.

Being able to talk to ourselves with compassion and forgiveness
• We are kind and loving toward ourselves.
• We embrace the truth about our human experience. Making mistakes is part of growth and learning.

Surrounding ourselves with beauty
• We celebrate beauty as a window into the divine and the eternal.
• We understand that by living with beauty, we accept living a life that does not support addictive behavior, but instead feeds our need for spiritual growth.

Developing relationships that help us develop our potential
• We radiate energies that reflect our spiritual beliefs and attract others who resonate with our essence.

Developing our creative drive
• We seek out and invest time in activities that contribute to our spiritual growth and make us feel creative, joyful, vital, and purposeful.

Feeling that we matter
• We embrace our divine nature and celebrate uniqueness.

Creating a support system for ourselves
• We choose to take our life journey with like-minded and nurturing spirits.

• We embrace the reality that we are not alone in our spiritual journey and that we belong to something greater and deeper than our overeating, fear, or shame.

Loving our bodies and seeing their good qualities
• Our bodies are wise and intelligent essences, the houses of our souls. They are entities that have been and will be with us during our entire earth-bound journey.

Following our intuition
• We are able to listen to the guidance of our intuition.
• We accept divine discontent as guidance toward necessary change in our spiritual development.
• We look for the lesson behind the food addiction, and we are open to the gift of learning to go beyond it.

Nourishing our spiritual being
• We feed our spiritual hunger.
• We long for the sense of connection to the divine, and we embrace our spiritual essence.
• We treasure our human experience and enjoy the lessons we learn that help to develop our spiritual being.
• We are sustained from within by our divinity.

We avoid comparing ourselves to others
• We are simultaneously unique and equal spiritual beings.

Trusting ourselves
• We trust our divine guidance, our hunches, our moments of inspiration, our sudden flashes of understanding and our premonitions.
• We celebrate experiences of grace.
• We trust the limitlessness of our divine selves.

Authority over ourselves, and refusal to give it away to others
• We take responsibility for the overall quality of our spiritual lives.

chapter 2: preparing for the journey

Self-love is not dependent on having husbands or wives, or on how well they are treating us. Self-love is not dependent on our children or how well they are behaving, or how they are doing in school. Self-love is not dependent on our friends, their kindness or lack of it, or their behaviors toward us. Self-love is not based on how well we are doing at home, at work, or in any other communities. Self-love is not dependent on any of our relationships, nor is it conditional upon external events, nor is it based on any special talents or feelings. Self-love is not fleeting or ethereal or temporal. It exists on its own merit. We either feel that we are worthy and deserve to take care of ourselves, or we are oblivious to the damage we do when our relationships and our feelings are dependent on the opinions of others or on external events.

Loving myself through actions, not just an intellectual understanding of self-love as a concept provided the power and the strength to transform. I stopped trying to fulfill my physical, emotional, intellectual and spiritual needs with food. Self-love led me to become my best advocate and my own best friend. This self-advocacy led to finding the causes behind my overeating behavior. I also began to understand that an important part of self-love was being with the pain of my emotions, that that facing these emotions would not shatter me. As the psalmist's prayer illustrated, I had to pass through the Valley of the Shadow. I had been discouraged; I had denied my pain; I had disowned myself, and I had to face the darkness of self-loathing. It was a difficult journey, but I emerged, embraced my spiritual self, and yearned for the friend I could be to me. I was committed, truly and profoundly, to being healthy, and if it took healing pain, so be it. I was ready.

When I experienced self-love and learned to be with my emotions, I was able to evaluate which foods were most healthy for me to eat. All my God-given gifts – physical, intellectual, emotional and spiritual – were aligned to support my best and deepest interest. The qualities and behaviors that I had been so willing to give to friends and family now became available to me.

A very important aspect of self-love is our ability to experience all our emotions, not just those that are celebrated in this society. When we experience the emotions we have been taught to reject, including emotions that are deemed undesirable, we stop suppressing an essential part of ourselves. When we stop repressing our own awareness – of dysfunctional overeating, of negative self-talk, and our hatred of our own bodies – we begin to experience genuine self-acceptance. Once I accepted all my feelings, I began to experience true self-love.

But there are other benefits of self-love aside from stopping the overeating behavior. Self-love increases the amount of love that we receive, thereby increasing our ability to love others. When we accept all our emotions, we find by extension the ability to accept emotions in other people. For example, if we celebrate ourselves in a situation in which we are assertive we tend to love other people when they are assertive.

We become more loving toward others because we accept dysfunctional traits that are common among us, and naturally, people will respond with their own love. They intuitively perceive our true self-acceptance. When people are deciding how they will respond to us, part of the decision is based on their perception of our own expectations. When we project energy and physical traits that manifest the reality "I am a person who can be loved," we are loved. Our self-love is confirmation that we are lovable, therefore we eagerly recognize and accept the love that is offered to us.

I am now and forever my own best friend. Finally and profoundly, learning self-love is a deeply personal journey to wholeness that ultimately heals emotional hunger.

body hate

I, like millions of American women, hated my body. My internal dialogue would go something like this: "I would pay money to have Jennifer Lopez's butt, mine is so huge... Man, I look like some thin women do when they are eight months pregnant... My stomach needs to be imprisoned inside a serious girdle... My arms are so flabby... I've begun to develop a second chin... My thighs look like tubes of cottage cheese." The internal self-loathing dialogue went on and on. I had heard that even being overweight, one should love one's body, but I thought whoever believed that was totally crazy! How could I possibly love a body with eighty pounds of extra FAT?

Everything in my socialization told me that being dissatisfied was the driving force behind achieving a goal. If I visualized getting that paycheck, I could endure working through difficult conditions. If I visualized how nice the house would feel, I could put in the four hours that it took to clean it. So the idea of loving my body, even when it was FAT was diametrically opposed to how I processed the world. I just couldn't bring myself to that experience.

chapter 2: preparing for the journey

When I thought about myself, I thought I was bright and insightful, but my identity resided totally above my shoulders. I lived seriously and permanently in my head. My body was what I needed to appear attractive and to be socially acceptable, I never thought of my body as having anything to do with who I was as a human being. As a consequence, I could hate my body and believe that I still had high self-esteem. I could hate my body and still value my skills, promote my achievements, and believe I was a good human being.

As I started to explore the correlation between emotional blockage and overeating, foreign words and concepts began to emerge. Words like energy centers, chakras, holding suppressed emotions. With much resistance and hesitation I began to consider that my body was also part of my being, my soul, who I was. That allowed me first to consider and finally to embrace the fact that my body is not only an integral part of who I am, but an integral part of the wisdom and the intelligence that I possess. Have you ever heard the saying "Trust your head but listen to your stomach?" Have you ever experienced an uncomfortable body sensation when something doesn't feel right, even when you can't express this feeling in a logical way? Have you ever been hungry when something is out of balance?

As I began appreciating my body, I gradually connected with it. I stopped thinking about it as a set of inadequate parts that didn't meet this society's standards of beauty. There is wisdom in the body that can heal. That is why whenever we are sick the most important prescription is rest. Let the innate intelligence of the body work for you to heal the shame of being FAT, of not being good enough. The body registers being rejected, and like any other intelligent essence it responds to rejection by getting worse. That is why dieting and exercise are not very effective when they are motivated by self-hate.

When I understood that the more I rejected my body the longer I would be trapped in my coat of fat, I apologized to my body. Then I began to take care of it as a grateful friend, with self-love and appreciation.

3 - understanding emotional hunger

how "different" people deal with their emotions

I'm sure you have a friend, or several, who never ever in their lives had a weight problem. You know, these are the people who tell you "When I'm upset I can't eat a thing." "When I'm sad I don't want to do anything, not even eat." "When I'm angry my stomach is so tight I couldn't put anything in it even if I wanted it."

For those of us with an emotional overeating behavior, these statements are so foreign that we really can't relate to them. When I'm tense I can't get the food into my mouth fast enough. When I'm sad all I want to do is eat in the hope of making myself feel better. When I'm angry the only thing that calms me down is food.

Obviously there is a huge difference between how one set of people deals with emotions and how we, the emotional eaters, deal with ours. My question was, "Why?" Why do certain people's stomachs shut down under emotional stress, while my group craves food as a means to cope, with the very same emotion?

Let us examine this difference more closely.

how fear might be experienced

Imagine two different people waiting at home for a phone call regarding a foreclosure decision on their mortgage. It is 3 A.M., and they can't sleep. They are in their kitchens dealing with the situation as best they know how. The first person, a rather thin and anxious man, is feeling terrified. He can't bear the thought of losing his house. He imagines vividly the impact on his family, on the quality of his life, the shame, the judgments of his friends and neighbors. He sits at the kitchen table overwhelmed by uncertainty, staring at his bills, terrified, despondent, paralyzed. These feelings so completely permeate his body that if anyone offered him something to eat, he would find it repulsive. His stomach, like the rest of his body, is tied in knots.

The second person is faced with the same situation. However this person is feeling a tremendous and overwhelming hunger. For some inexplicable reason he is famished. He doesn't understand why he is so

37

hungry, he just knows that he must have something to eat, and the desire is so strong that it is only second to the need to breathe. He goes to the refrigerator and starts eating directly from the shelves. He doesn't seem to be able to get the food into his mouth quickly enough. As he is chewing one piece of food, he is already considering what else he can eat. His situation is as serious as the thin person's, but while he is enjoying the pleasure of the food he doesn't have to experience the anxiety and pain. He is mostly suppressing the stress of the situation with the temporary high afforded by food. Food is the narcotic that has anaesthetized an unbearable pain. His face reflects the contentment he feels while eating.

how frustration might be experienced

Imagine a corporate luncheon in an office meeting room. Difficult issues being discussed. Disagreement among coworkers ensues, and everyone is trying to justify to the boss that it was not their fault the project has failed. The boss is confronting everyone regarding the devastating results. One of the people facing the confrontation and accusations is a project manager. An overwhelming sense of frustration permeates his body. The feeling emanates from below his abdomen, directly from his sexual organs. When this feeling fully radiates, it seems to constrict all the muscles in his body, particularly the stomach muscles. While there is a sumptuous and appealing buffet laid out in the conference room, his feelings of frustration are so intense and palpable that every single muscle in his body feels affected. The idea of having to digest anything is revolting. He is not only ignoring the food, he just wishes someone would take it away.

Another person, who knows that she is next in line to be confronted and interrogated, finds herself suddenly unable to stop thinking about food. The food becomes a magnetic force that distracts her from the arguments at hand and the strong emotions that others are expressing. She keeps thinking of how tasty and pleasurable a triple-decker sandwich is going to be. She longs for the arguments to end so she can savor all the glorious food before her. Since it is a lunch meeting, she disengages from the fighting and begins to assemble the most nurturing and delicious plate she can. She lovingly and longingly selects her food and tries to enjoy as much of it as possible while marginally engaging in the discussion. The thoughts might go something like this: "Boy, this pumpernickel bread is fresh, and the smoked ham and Swiss cheese are heavenly with the Dijon mustard. Ahhh, the crispy vegetables really bring out the flavors of all of these deli meats. As soon as I finish this sandwich, I'm going to enjoy a piece of that luscious cheesecake."

how anger might be experienced

A highly emotional person is caught in an important meeting. It's late, and the meeting shows no signs of ending any time soon. He had planned to take off early that day and now finds himself leaving at the height of rush hour. He is scheduled to catch a flight and spend the weekend meeting his fiancée's parents. As he had dreaded, he is now stuck in a traffic jam. The radio reports congestion on all the routes to the airport. He is livid. "Why, oh why, did I agree to participate in that stupid meeting"? Well, it wasn't stupid, it was very important to his career. But he cannot miss that flight! This weekend is just too important. His fiancée might call the whole thing off if he doesn't make it, and this is the last flight to that small town in the boondocks where his future in-laws live. He is angrily leaning on his horn because most of the delay is being caused by rubbernecks who don't seem to have a life and need to indulge in a gory traffic accident. He could kill these people. This is just so unfair. What options does he have? Thoughts of food do not even enter his mind.

An emotional eater caught in the same situation might experience swaying hunger pangs and find himself distracted by the signs of the restaurants and fast food establishments visible from the highway. He doesn't understand the urgency of the hunger he is experiencing. He savors the taste of an imagined hamburger. He thinks to himself, "It would only take a couple minutes to get a Monster Burger, and it would help me get out of this traffic. Actually, if I get off at the next exit I can zip through the drive-through, get a Monster Burger, take the alternate route to the airport, and probably get there faster."

how grief might be experienced

Imagine a funeral parlor. The deceased, a young man in his mid-thirties, has died tragically in an automobile accident. His wife of three years sits by the casket distraught, bewildered, confused, dazed and saddened beyond comprehension or words. Nothing seems to console her. The love of her life, the man she dreamed she would grow old with, is gone. The man who was her friend, her support, her reason for living has ceased to exist. Her grief is profound. There is no experience of hunger, no desire to eat, she can't sleep, and she begins to feel that there is no point in living. She has not only lost her appetite, her body doesn't seem to want anything.

Let's imagine a different spouse under the same circumstances. As she is told of the terrible tragedy, she first goes into denial and laughs at the idea that her husband, the vivacious, resourceful man that she married, would let such an accident happen to him. Surely the police made a mistake. They've confused her husband with someone else. As she approaches the body, she has no choice but to stop denying the possibility that it is her husband after all. She takes the event well and suddenly grows hungry as she begins to make plans and mentally list the many phone calls that need to be made to relatives, coworkers and neighbors. When she gets home she makes herself a delicious sandwich as she attends to the many details of funeral arrangements, cemetery selection, where to hold the wake, what foods to serve. During the funeral, she lets people console her and later at the buffet, she plays the gracious hostess. Every time she goes to the buffet table, she samples this meat, or that dessert, just to make sure everything is satisfactory.

emotional people versus emotional eaters

As depicted in the previous scenarios, it is obvious that there are different ways to experience the same emotion. For emotional eaters, many feelings lead to urgent and inexplicable hunger. For most emotional people, the intensity of emotions usually means the disappearance of hunger. The idea of eating when they are sad, angry, frustrated or grieving is completely foreign to them. Their emotions are experienced in such a physical manner that they don't coexist with hunger. The energy generated by these emotions takes over the body and interferes with many normal functions, such as physical hunger. Even the muscles, especially the stomach muscles, contract, further inhibiting any desire for food. While they are experiencing strong emotions, physical hunger doesn't manifest in the body. This condition lasts until the emotion has dissipated.

In contrast, the emotional eater does not seem to be able to fully experience emotions at the same level of intensity. There is an undercurrent, a vague manifestation of the emotion that is accompanied by an overwhelming desire for the pleasure of food. In essence, the profound sadness is suppressed, and the driving need becomes a search for relief, a quest to mitigate the emotional pain with the comfort of food. Let us examine the mechanism that causes many of us to suppress our emotions.

what are suppressed/repressed emotions?

As a person privileged to be a citizen of the United States, a great deal of my socialization involved the avoidance of any discomfort or inconvenience. I was socialized to take aspirin for headaches, Midol™ for cramps, coffee when I was tired, and an epidural during labor. I demanded first-class airline seating, the best cushion for my backside, stadium seating to truly enjoy a movie, and a recliner for TV viewing. My hands were never to experience discomfort even while doing dishes. My son, at the tender age of fourteen, was already suggesting that we needed to get a car with heated seats so that we didn't have to experience three minutes of discomfort on a cold winter morning. The American marketing industry is predicated on the core belief that there is always something we can do or take to avoid, or at the very least mitigate any discomfort. I was never taught, encouraged, or counseled regarding the benefits of experiencing the discomfort of my emotions. I wonder if this is why I started to crave something to eat whenever I felt any hint of emotional uneasiness.

Repression is similar to suppression in that the emotion is not expressed. In repression, we deny that the emotion even exists. The repressed emotion is blocked because it has been judged disruptive to our psychological stability or our self-image. However, both the stability and the self-image are illusory because they are based on a rejection of our own emotions.

The negative aspect of repression is that the emotions remain unperceived, or for an emotional eater, energized as hunger. The suppressed or repressed emotions continue to exert influence, in our case via the overeating behavior, while they push for expression. Although suppression can cause tension and conflict, repression can cause even more damage because our lack of awareness means we have less ability to recognize how it is harming us.

When we learn to repress emotions, our perceptions are distorted. If the mechanism of repression is food, it projects through our bodies as emotional hunger. Because we do not perceive our emotions accurately, we interpret information from our surroundings inaccurately, and thus we respond inappropriately; we react with hunger to situations we cannot emotionally address. Repression distorts not only our observations in the moment, but also our memories of the past and our expectations for the future.

Repressed material is not available for our use. Every thought and emotion has a potential purpose, perhaps offering new perspective, vitality, or a broader understanding of our wholeness. When we repress, we are refusing self-knowledge. If we deny our fear, for example, we are not able to use the adrenaline energy that is associated with it, nor can we have full awareness of the dangers triggering the fear.

Repression prevents us from understanding ourselves. For example, if we examine our selfishness instead of pretending that it doesn't exist, we might find the causes for our behavior. Perhaps we will discover that selfishness is actually a reasonable response to people who are abusing our generosity. When repressed emotions remain unresolved, we eat instead of admitting that an emotion exists. By shifting our focus from the emotion to satisfying the inexplicable hunger, we can't take action toward a solution that would address the repressed emotion. Over a period of time, those emotions degenerate into more acceptable emotions; for example, when we stuff our anger with food, we feel resentment or bitterness, but these negative feelings are insidiously directed toward ourselves, and not toward the person or situation or circumstance that has triggered the anger.

Repressed emotions cause physical distress due to repressed energy lodged in the body. It might be experienced as physical tension, numbness, lack of vitality, depression, diminished body awareness and, eventually, illness. Massage therapists and other body workers know that when their treatments release physical stress, clients often feel an upsurge of inexplicable emotions – emotions that have been locked in their tissues.

Repressed emotions consume energy. The effort to keep material in the unconscious mind is like trying to keep a buoyant object underwater; we are eating to hold back the energy of the repressed elements. When repressed material is released, we might experience a feeling of lightness, freedom and power, because the energy from the emotion and from our effort to repress it is now available for constructive use.

Repression causes emotional numbness. We repress by intellectually denying the reality of the emotion and by desensitizing ourselves to the movement and pressure of the emotional energy within us. To the extent that we repress negative emotions or sensations, we are simultaneously repressing our capacity to feel positive emotions or sensations. For example, when we stuff our fear and anger with food, we also lose our capacity to feel true happiness and pleasure.

To the extent that we suppress our feelings, we inhibit normal emotional development. When a repressed emotion finally bursts out, it does so in an immature form. Chronically repressed anger, for instance, expresses as a temper tantrum. The expression of anger can also regress and become primitive and unfocused as it degenerates into a general, vague hostility.

The reaction to repressed emotions becomes automatic, and overeating takes on a life of its own. For emotional eaters, work breaks are automatically associated with food. Instead of messages such as: "You are physically at your limit; take a walk around the block," the message is: "You are hungry. Go to the vending machine and buy a snack." Because the ego has denied its connection to our feelings, it does not accept them. Consequently the reaction to the emotion automatically drives us into compulsive overeating. As the ego makes plans and designs its life, the repressed emotions seem to develop agendas of their own, as if plotting a way to express themselves. But their expression will necessarily be contrary to our conscious will, as though an alien force is imposing itself. The repressed emotions are projected more intensely, and we see people through distorted perceptions. The result can cause a reversal in our behavior. Jung used the term "enantiodromia." This is a technical term that expresses the inclination of people to go from one extreme to the other, as when a seemingly agreeable, sweet and harmless person suddenly indulges in a violent rampage.

why are emotions repressed or suppressed?

For many of us, suppressing emotions is learned from childhood as part of our socialization. My personal experience is that most major corporations reward denial of emotions and personal needs. I had been trained to work past exhaustion, completely stressed out, accommodating the demands of difficult people, oblivious to my own feelings and needs. I'm sure you have heard praise for those who "know how to keep cool in dire situations." I was rewarded for ignoring my needs. I was celebrated because I was able to work when others were ready to give up. I was promoted for having the drive to set my feelings aside. The message from school and work was, "Work hard. You can always do better, do more. Push yourself." I never understood that I was also learning to discard the messages my body was sending, and in the long run to suppress my emotions.

In addition, I had a history of childhood neglect, so the ability to get in touch with what I needed or felt was completely foreign to me. Finally, my body and emotional awareness were totally compromised. I remember going to an eating disorder therapist and being confused when she asked me, "How do you feel when you are hungry?" She had a chart of different emotions from which I was supposed to choose. I had no clue. I explained to her that it was difficult for me to be in touch with my emotions. She then asked me to guess. Somehow that was not very satisfying or effective. I did not feel better when I guessed that I was bored. Much later I discovered that I was lonely.

It took me four more years to learn that there were ways to get in touch with my emotions. I kept asking myself why, although I had the intelligence, drive and willpower to manage multimillion-dollar projects, I could not lose weight. I began to consider other alternatives outside of "the body reflects the mind" Western psychological values. When I had tried and failed with so many diets, personal trainers, psychotherapists even psychologists who specialized in eating-disorders, I began to ask why I didn't have access to my feelings.

And here is the question: Why are some people in touch with their emotions while others of us are not? Although I can't answer that question for everyone, I can share my experience of how I became emotionally detached.

Like most Latin American parents, mine were caring and hard-working people. My father was the eighth child of twelve reared in a poor family. I never heard that my father went hungry, though in a household with so many children and few resources, nurturing was not something my father learned. He learned to fend for himself and make his own way in the world. The family story told about my father was that he was such a troublemaker when he was little that he got thrown out of second grade and never went back to school, but I had a difficult time understanding why he never received an education.

My mother's story was worse. Her mother, a very attractive wandering gypsy, had six children by six different men, none of whom she married. My mother, the fourth of these children, was given in servitude to one of her aunts. She was given food and shelter in exchange for which she was expected to work around the clock and was never sent to school. My mother learned how to read and write because the children of her adopted household taught her.

Looking back, I can understand the attraction between my mother and father. My father was a man of the street, a man determined to make his fortune in the world. My mother needed anything to take her out of slavery. She wanted a man who had dreams – a man who would build a home for them. But at the end of the day, they were both severely neglected children.

The household into which I was born was clean, ambitious, and driven. Both parents were always working toward that better house, higher status, more servants. They worked hard so their children had the one thing they never received – an education. They provided not merely an education, but the very best education money could buy. From day one, my siblings and I were sent to private schools. Because of their hard work, my parents' household thrived and finally became prosperous. We had nannies, cooks and chauffeurs. In fact, my mother didn't learn how to drive until my father's death, some 18 years after they married.

I was never hurt, beaten or abused in any manner. Our house was filled with lovely things, but I don't remember my parents being there; they were always working. I don't remember that they ever helped me with my homework. How could they? They hardly had an education themselves. I don't remember ever feeling that I was special, ever being asked how I felt or what I thought about anything or what I wanted for Christmas. I do remember how elated my parents were when the report cards came home. With the exception of my middle sister, the rebel of the family, the rest of us understood that getting good grades was tantamount to love.

Considering my parents' educational background and how they grew up in non-nurturing environments, it is astonishing how much they did accomplish. Our household never lacked material goods. We went on to get advanced graduate degrees, medical degrees, and law degrees. We had families of our own. We were successful. But after so many years of asking, "Why do I have this destructive overeating behavior?" "Why the addiction?" – after going to a handful of psychologists, all of whom kept asking, "What was your family life like? What do you remember about your childhood? Tell me about your parents." – I understood that my childhood experiences had formed my addictive behavior.

Dilia De La Altagracia

Part of the search for an end to my addiction led me to an "Inner Child" workshop, one of those intensive weekends with much revisiting, introspection and analysis of childhood experiences. One memorable exercise occurred when the workshop facilitator asked us "What were the messages that you received as a child?" People began shouting different phrases that the facilitator promptly wrote on the board:

- "You are stupid."
- "You are clumsy."
- "You'll never amount to anything."
- "You're such a cry-baby."
- "You have no talent."

The list went on and on. I remember just sitting there wracking my brain trying to remember what messages I had received as a child and, frankly, coming up blank. Finally someone else asked, "What if you didn't get any messages? What if your parents were not around?" One of the participants yelled out, "That's called neglect!"

Up to that moment in my life, it had never occurred to me that I had been neglected. The very notion that my parents were neglectful was completely repulsive to me. They had worked so hard, they loved us so much, and they had sacrificed everything for us. But slowly, without blaming my parents, I have come to understand the importance of being nurtured. As children, having our needs met, having our worries attended to, having our little hurts comforted, having our silly stories listened to, having the bogeyman shooed away is what connects us to our feelings. When we experience childhood without nurturing parents, we don't learn that we have feelings or that our feelings matter, and we become detached from our own feelings. After eating most of my emotions, I finally understood that being in touch with feelings is vital to being a fully functioning human being.

The insight that I gained during this inner child workshop was invaluable. Other people understood the source of their anger and feelings of inadequacy. I learned one of the critical developmental reasons why I'd been detached from my feelings all my life. I seldom expressed anger, I never yelled at anyone, I was never demanding. I was always the agreeable, chubby woman who would drop whatever she was doing to help others. I began to understand why I always put other people's feelings above my own: I believed that if I could help them, maybe they would like me.

chapter 3: understanding emotional hunger

I cried a lot during that weekend, and the release was very helpful. I finally understood that access to my feelings had been compromised by my childhood experiences. However, that information did not stop the hunger. Understanding never does. At least with this newly gained insight, I began to search for anything that would help me get in touch with my feelings.

how emotions are stored in the body

"People mistakenly assume that their thinking is done by their head; it is actually done by the heart, which first dictates the conclusion, then commands the head to provide the reasoning that will defend it."

- Tony De Mello

For most of my life I had been identified as "a thinking person." My demeanor and persona conveyed the message that all problems can be solved with brain power. I considered any notion that emotions are stored in the body airy-fairy nonsense. Why are emotions stored in the body? How are emotions stored in the body? Why can't the mind dissipate emotions?

Unbeknownst to most of us, our bodies absorb our life experiences. Our bodies are our archives, meticulously recording every joy and sorrow, as well as storing every emotion not fully experienced. A burgeoning body of research attests to this fact.

We are learning that illnesses such as heart disease, chronic pain, cancer, thyroid disorders and irritable bowel syndrome can all have their roots in neuropeptide links originating in the brain. In her book, *Molecules of Emotions*, Candace Pert, Ph.D., proved the existence of neuropeptides in the body, which carry thoughts and emotions formed in the brain to cells and organs throughout the body.

In *The Body Bears the Burden*, Robert C. Scaer, M.D., describes how the body recognizes and stores traumatic memories through biochemical and neuroendocrine changes. Peter Levine, M.D., in *Waking the Tiger* documents the physiological changes which occur during emotionally charged events and how these changes persist long after the event is over if they are not discharged and released. They literally "freeze" in the body.

Scientists have also studied the body's responses while a person views a violent TV show and then compared those to the body's experiences

47

listening to Mozart. There are clear differences. Positive energy enhances our cellular energy. Allowing for joy, hope and encouragement in our lives literally brings nutrients into our cells, raises our metabolic rate and releases the freeze response, which in turn moves our cells away from biological death. One of the best known examples of this is Dr. Dean Ornish's *Opening Your Heart* program which he proved that heart disease can be reversed in people with Type A personalities who undergo lifestyle changes physically, emotionally and spiritually.

The fact is that we are being impacted on the cellular level by the daily events in our lives, and have been since we were born. As Caroline Myss says, "Your biography is your biology."

After reluctantly entertaining the possibility that emotions might be held in our bodies, I began to study the concept of energy centers. I discovered that this is not a concept invented in the past thirty years by the New Age community. The Hindu yoga masters identified where our emotional energies seemed to concentrate and named them chakras, a Sanskrit word that translates as "wheel." Perhaps an even better translation would be "spinning wheel." These are locations within our bodies that have been studied for thousands of years. In fact, the word chakra originated with the Vedic teachings of ancient India nearly 5,000 years ago.

chapter 3: understanding emotional hunger

This illustration depicts the energy centers and their locations:

The concept of an energy center does not mean that we don't feel energy and associated emotions anywhere else in the body; it simply means that this is the approximate location where specific emotions seem to be most acutely experienced. If the chakra is open, balanced, and freely flowing, we experience emotions immediately and intensely. If the center is clogged, out of balance, or blocked, we tend to suppress our emotions. However, suppression doesn't mean that none of the emotion is experienced since it is not possible to completely block the energy of emotion. In later chapters we will discuss in further detail how suppressed emotions drive our overeating behavior.

Once I stopped pooh-poohing the notion that there might be some wisdom in the concept of chakras and entertained the possibility of their validity, a new world of understanding opened to me.

how our emotions are processed

There are seven chakras or energy centers. The following is a list of the first five centers and the emotions that are associated with each[5].

Survival Center

Associated color: Red

Location: Where the perineum and coccyx meet near the base of the spine

Emotions: Fear in general, but more specifically, fear resulting from the threat of material loss, lack, bodily injury and disease or death; general anxiety, possessiveness, selfishness, insecurity, paranoia; the sense of limitation or delay; having physical or psychological boundaries invaded; the desire for protection, safety, and basic survival.

Sensation Center

Associated color: Orange

Location: Sexual organs

Emotions: Sexual desire, frustration, compulsiveness, violation, inhibition, revulsion; cravings and frustrated desires for touch, food, TV, alcohol, drugs, smoking, entertainment, and the physical sensations that frustration may bring up.

chapter 3: understanding emotional hunger

Power Center

Associated color: Yellow

Location: The solar plexus above the navel and below the breasts

Emotions: Anger, aggressiveness, hostility, frustration; the sense of worthlessness, inadequacy, helplessness, weakness, emptiness; feelings of being blocked by others or by circumstances, being used, manipulated or cheated, being blamed or mistreated; not getting deserved credit; the desire for significance or importance, the desire for approval, recognition, and attention, the desire for influence over others, the desire for control; the pain of not having gotten the father love you needed.

Heart Center

Associated color: Emerald green with a Pink heart center

Location: Between the breasts

Emotions: Loneliness, isolation, sadness, shame, heartbreak, jealousy; grief over the loss of others; being abandoned, not being taken care of, not receiving the love you need, not being accepted; being hated or hating others; the desire for love, acceptance, belonging; feelings related to the mother and the feminine side of the character in general; feelings of not having gotten the mother love you needed.

Creative Center

Associated color: Blue

Location: Throat.

Emotions: Self-expression, inner emptiness from unrealized creative work, being creatively blocked, the desire to create or express.

Along with these five energy centers, there are the Intuitive and the Spiritual chakras. However, these higher centers are associated with spiritual and intuitive functions and their flow and balance are typically not discussed in the context of physical addictions. These two upper energy centers might affect spiritual, intellectual or dogmatic rigidity. Consequently they will not be covered in this book.

Once I understood which centers were associated with specific feelings, I made a list of the emotions that were recurring in my life. I kept a journal and correlated how these recurring emotions were influencing my overeating behavior.

Compulsiveness
• Compulsiveness has been a major personality trait all my life. When I decided to sing jazz, I went to jazz clubs twice a week. I studied with musicians at least once a week, and in one year I compiled a book of 100 songs in my vocal range. A book of this magnitude takes most singers at least three years to compile.
• If I decided to prepare meals from a specific cookbook, I would select ten recipes, organize the ingredients in a database, cross-reference the list with ingredients already in my kitchen and purchase the remaining ingredients for these recipes the very next day.
• The concept of balance has been elusive all my life, so when I overate, it was in a hideous, compulsive manner that could only be called a frenzy. Is there such a thing as a non-compulsive binge? We all occasionally indulge in something we shouldn't eat, but if the compulsive element could be removed, I probably would stop after a few bites.

Cravings
• I had cravings for specific foods when I suppressed certain feelings. I craved chocolate for the blues, ice cream for loneliness, nachos for boredom, pizza for disappointment, coffee with lots of cream when I was tired, and anything crunchy for anxiety. Obviously, an eradication of the cravings would be a good indication that my food addiction was beginning to heal.

Frustration
• Food was a good consolation prize and a great distraction to make me forget frustration.

Worthlessness
• When I felt worthless, I would eat something delicious to engage in a satisfying experience and mask my feelings.

chapter 3: understanding emotional hunger

Not getting the credit I deserve
• When I felt overlooked, I consoled myself with food.

Desire for significance
• All my life I have wanted to feel above average, to know that what I do matters in the world. I remember having a discussion in high school about our greatest fear and I said, "To die without making a difference in the world." So much of life is occupied with the daily struggle to maintain our infrastructure and meet our basic needs –bathing, cooking, cleaning, getting our children to all of their activities, making sure that their needs are met. It was difficult for me to have a sense of worth when, at the end of the day, all I had accomplished were these essentials of life. This makes me feel empty. When I feel this way, food seemed to plug the emotional hole.

Desire for approval
• Whenever I did anything, even something insignificant, I always wanted to show it to someone. At work my bosses usually didn't ask for a status report because the moment I completed anything I would show it to them. I know that some people are introverted, but I needed to have people share in my excitement to give me a sense that what I'd done was worthwhile. Whenever I attempted to share my excitement and it was not reflected back, I needed to eat to celebrate my accomplishment.

Recognition
• I remember one job in which a co-worker kept taking my ideas and passing them off as his. Every time he did this, I was furious. But I did not acknowledge my anger or express it to anyone else. I never confronted him or even made a joke about it. I just ate through the lack of recognition.

Inadequacy
• For so much of my life I've felt inadequate, the body is such a tangible part of our humanity that just showing up FAT brought forward the weighty sense of shame that I felt about myself. The moment I arrived at most activities I wondered where was the buffet table, where was the courtesy bar, what was being served as an entrée, where and when could I hide behind the pleasure of food.

Dilia De La Altagracia

Pain of not getting the fathering I needed
• For many years I was a workaholic. I pushed myself hard at the office, gave up many weekends for the needs of the corporation, went to work even when I was sick, and placed my work ahead of my son. It took years of therapy to understand that the workaholic behavior was nothing more than my need to get the recognition from my bosses that I never received from my father.

Loneliness
• One of the most consistent overeating triggers was coming home. Even after I'd had a sumptuous five-course dinner, walking into an empty house automatically caused a hunger that I was never able to explain.

Shame
• Being fat has been a tremendous source of shame. The paradox is that I ate to feel better.

Grief over loss and death
• The death of my parents, especially my father, has always been a source of unabated pain. Anytime there is a conversation about death, or I see any of my friends deal with the loss of a loved one, or even when death is portrayed in a movie, I have an overwhelming feeling of grief. My first reaction used to be to eat something to make me feel better.

Being abandoned
• My father died when I was seventeen. My mother didn't speak English, didn't know how to drive, and didn't know how to run the finances of the household. As the oldest child, I was pushed into the role of pseudo-parent. I felt abandoned by my father and ill prepared for the tasks that I was asked to execute after his death.
• My ex-husband left me when my son was five months old. I comforted myself with food and experienced the largest weight gain of my life, 70 pounds within four months of his departure.
• The one issue that cuts me to the heart is when friends let me down. This generates a sense of incomprehensible and consuming abandonment. It is very difficult for me to express these feelings to my friends, so I usually eat through these periods.

chapter 3: understanding emotional hunger

The desire for love
• I love chick flicks. I especially love the warm and fuzzy feeling of "some day my prince will come," particularly when I'm sharing these feelings with Mr. Häagen Dazs™ or a nice plate of nachos.

Acceptance
• It is always difficult for me to accept my accomplishments. I always feel that I could do more, or do better, or improve on this or that. It is so rare that I really embrace something and feel, "Yes! I did this and it is great! It is wonderful and I'm so proud of it." I never have a sense of acceptance of myself, of my work, of my home. There is always something else that could be done to make it better, to improve on it. Because I don't allow a sense of accomplishment fill me I use food to make me feel satisfied.

Belonging
A quote by Lorraine Hansberry states, "The thing that makes you exceptional is inevitably that which must also make you lonely."

• Despite my many talents, I have always had a sensation of not belonging, even in a group of friends. In high school and college I never belonged to any organized clubs. I have produced social events such as jazz performances and lavish parties, but I was the organizer or the hostess. The sense of not belonging then fuels the loneliness that is comforted with food.

Being used
Several studies have correlated childhood sexual molestation with eating disorders. For the compulsive overeater, delight from food is a highly controlled pleasure in a world where we have experienced so profound a violation of basic boundaries. There is the illusion that we can always count on getting what we want from food – love, comfort, excitement, nurturing. Name an emotional need and there is a food that will simulate fulfillment of that need. And when we don't know how to get needs met, food is the dependable and safe surrogate.

The premise of these studies is that violation of boundaries at an early age leads to dysfunctional construction of personal boundaries later in life. For many adults, early traumatic experiences translate into a dysfunctional body image, which in many cases leads to an overwhelming need for protection. Our bodies become a solid and tangible boundary, in essence a fat coat, and we must protect ourselves against being too attractive and the unwanted advances that being sexy would bring. At a subconscious level, somewhere in our personal development, fat is equated with safety.

If you were sexually molested as a child, or began sexual activity at an inappropriate age, it might be worthwhile to explore these childhood experiences with a trained professional.

exercise:

Create your own list of recurring emotions that lead to over-eating, and journal how these emotions affect your overeating behavior.

4 - **tools for the journey**

Here is the good news: There are tools that help us sit and be with our emotions. (Thank God. I was ready to throw this book out the window!)

tools for developing self-love

1. Face your critical inner parent – Become aware of your negative inner judgments. Take action to eradicate shame from your life. Shame is the belief that there is something innately wrong and undeserving in us. Gain awareness of how the belief was formed. Take steps to change the belief and remove any reinforcing messages that keep you ashamed. For example, mainstream marketing conveys the message that outer beauty makes a woman worthwhile. In many cases beauty itself has been narrowly defined as a specific dress size or specific facial features. When we endorse and then consume a steady diet of magazines, news and advertising that feeds us a polished and fabricated concept of beauty, it is unlikely that we will celebrate ourselves because mere mortals do not measure up to those standards. Awareness begins when we acknowledge our own internal critical thoughts. We need a concrete and measurable way to increase recognition of our mental drainage. One very effective and tangible method is to begin the day with a pocket full of quarters. Every time you have a debilitating self-critique, move one quarter to the "count pocket." At the end of the day move that money to a jar. The money can be donated to your favorite charity or used to participate in any activity that would help eradicate negative thinking.

2. Take risks – A wounded self-esteem is like a physical wound, and we find ourselves avoiding any activity that might bring to the surface the pain of self-rejection. We find that we take fewer risks in our social lives, in our career options, in our family relationships. However, when we over-protect even a physical wound, the muscle around it atrophies. It takes longer for the wound to heal because it lacks the supporting structure to function properly. Being human entails growth, making mistakes and taking risks. We dishonor ourselves when we deny the nature of our humanity and our need to grow.

3. Celebrate who you are – When we are in love, the world seems a vibrant place. The sunset is more radiant, we discover qualities in others we never saw before, we feel joyful and alive. Celebrating who we are brings some of the same experience into our lives. Get to know who you truly are, that unique representation that has manifested in this time on Earth as you. When we appreciate who we are, we feel blessed and grateful, we are awake and vital, we are aware of our gifts. We can project contentment, satisfaction, gratitude and happiness. We are excited about the possibilities that the future holds.

4. Make yourself a priority – Words are cheap, intentions are worthless, desires are empty dreams if we don't take action to care for our physical, emotional, intellectual and spiritual needs. In whatever fashion you allocate your time, be it a list of tasks, appointments on a calendar, or reviewing lunch options with a friend, ask yourself, "Have I met my physical, emotional, intellectual and spiritual needs? Am I a priority in my life? Do my activities reflect this belief?"

5. Inventory your qualities – Write on a card a list of your qualities, what you like about yourself. If you have difficulty with this task, ask friends and family what qualities they like about you. Keep this card with you at all times.

6. Begin the day powerfully – The intentions you set in the morning determine what you will accomplish during the day. Intentions are not a list of activities but powerful feelings and attitudes associated with each of the activities. If you schedule a workout but the intentions are tentative, conditional, accompanied with a sense of despondency, if there is no joy associated with this activity – such as the celebration that you are taking care of yourself, the anticipation of feeling vital – it is not likely that you will make it to the gym. That is why many people who want to lose weight don't seem to carry out the very activities that are needed to achieve this objective. Schedule your activities accompanied by powerful emotions to ensure that you will follow through.

7. End the day with a grateful heart – Everything emanates from grace. Having a grateful heart, not only for present gifts, but also for imminent blessings, ensures the manifestation of an authentic self. The end of the day, the time right before surrendering to tranquility, is a perfect opportunity to give thanks for who you are and for honoring your desire to be healthy.

8. Develop a weekly self-love plan – Make a list of what you can do this week to take care of your physical, mental, intellectual, and spiritual needs.   Assess how you did last week and move any unaccomplished items to the new calendar. Amend the list with a powerful intention for each activity.

9. Effective manifestation – We can visualize taking the step that will ensure we are practicing self-love, taking care of our physical, emotional, intellectual and spiritual needs. We visualize not just doing the activities that keep us vital, growing, vibrant and sentient, but also scheduling the time.

10. Extend the qualities of love toward ourselves – For example, develop positive qualities including self-acceptance, patience, generosity, forgiveness, and self-respect.

11. Commit to knowing yourself – Self-discovery is the key. Who are we when we strip away the layers of socialization, education and fear? Who are we when we look beneath the daily events of our lives and examine those long neglected parts of ourselves to find the deeper issues lying below? What are our strengths? What makes us happy? What are the shadows that we refuse to acknowledge? Could you write a page about who you are without mentioning your social status, how many children you have, or where you live? How much time elapses between the time that you are introduced to a new person and the time you tell them what you do for a living? Who are you?

12. Learn to laugh at yourself – There is more humor available in observing our mistakes than in observing our successes. If we miss these opportunities, we lose our humanity and our balance. Problems arise from being over-earnest, and we endow ourselves, our causes, or situations with unnecessary seriousness. Overly solemn people can become especially vulnerable to the heavy burden of their preoccupations. The ability to see humor in our experiences, to laugh in the face of a dire world – what is called black humor – these attitudes are helpful in not becoming too tightly wound. Part of the daily tension in so many lives is the intense wish that things were different.

journaling

Journaling is a non-analytical approach to self-discovery. Journaling is a different activity than keeping a personal diary, it is instead spiritual witnessing. Whereas a personal diary records events and our feelings about them, journaling is about gain insight into ourselves. Better self-knowledge can help one discover and overcome anxieties and misperceptions about oneself and/or life. This, in turn, can help one improve satisfaction with life, inter-personal relationships, and one's ability to function in his/her everyday life. We drop underneath the daily problems examining those parts of ourselves long neglected to find the deeper issues lying below. In the unfolding process of journaling, self-discovery awaken and then healing. In the journal writing we are working in the direction towards our authentic self, a self not defined by popular media or the dulling effect of mindless activities.

breathing

"At the pace of creation, all things breathe the same way. So when we slow and open and center ourselves, we breathe with all of life, and breathing this way we draw the strength from all of life."

– Mark Nepo

There is one simple fact of which most people are unaware: Breathing is responsible for 70% of the body's elimination system. The act of breathing processes stress and toxins. Another statistic you may find interesting is that most people breathe at only 20% of their capacity, which means that the respiratory system is handling only 14% of the body's elimination needs. Because our breathing is so limited, we have in effect compromised the elimination system by approximately half. With this knowledge, when we realize the benefits of integrating more effective breathing we realize that it is one of the best investments we can make in ourselves.

Breathing, when done correctly, can aid us in getting in touch with our emotions. Through my research I've discovered that shallow breathing interferes with the flow of emotions. I was so ashamed of my stomach because it didn't meet social standards, that I spent most of my time holding it in; it became second nature to have a constricted stomach. As a result I stopped breathing deeply. Even in situations where I was supposed to breathe deeply, such as yoga classes, my socialization was so ingrained that I had difficulty letting go of muscles that had been molded to unnatural limits. When I started getting in touch with my emotions, I noticed that my breathing began to deepen.

Breathing is the quickest way to relax, but it is much more than that. Breathing facilitates becoming reconnected to our bodies, and by extension sensing our emotions. It facilitates emotional mastery, particularly over anxiety, the number one reason preventing most of us from being with our emotions. Again, it is the difference between relaxing before the injection or tensing all our muscles as the needle enters. As the essential life-force function of the body, deep breathing is one of the most effective ways of getting in touch with our emotions. Healing breaths are deep, even, and fluid. Suppressed breathing is shallow, jerky and short; consequently, the oxygen can't reach all parts of the body. Intentions help get in touch with our inner wisdom. We can breathe into the hunger. There we have access to our healing solutions. Unlike any other healing technique, breathing does not require special clothing, going to a class, or a quiet place. Breathing is abundant, and you can do it when you need it, as you need it.

If you practice yoga you will hear over and over that yoga is the marriage between movement and breathing. The key to most yoga poses is to breathe through the anxiety we feel when we contort our bodies into uncomfortable or unfamiliar positions. Likewise a key aspect of healing emotional hunger is to stay with the emotion until it dissipates. Every time we recognize that there is emotional imbalance, breathing is one of the most effective aids to help stay with the discomfort of the emotions so we don't have to run to the refrigerator to suppress them. Only when we breathe during our anxiety, our disappointment, our anger, our loneliness can we stay with these emotions. But we must breathe in a healing fashion – not the shallow, rapid breath of "fight or flight" that further fuels anxiety, but the deep – pause after the intake and pause after the exhale – healing breath that nurtures and calms.

So breathe deeply, breathe with healing intention, breathe into the anxiety and express your desire to be with your emotions; express your desire to experience whatever hides behind the hunger. Keep breathing deeply and evenly until the hunger has expressed itself in your body and you are conscious and in touch with what is truly going on within.

Today I understand that the very act of holding in my belly for such a long time was detrimental to my ability to get in touch with my emotions. When we are scared we tighten our stomach muscles, the breath goes into the chest, and we lose our ability to be open to ourselves. Shallow breathing is the fight-or-flight response that puts us into survival mode. In most social and work situations, we can't run from the room, nor can we punch the irritating person who is making us crazy. It is critical to stop fight-or-flight breathing. Instead, breathe deeply, slowly, and evenly; expand every single muscle of the stomach wall and chest cavity. This type of breathing nurtures and allows us to stay in a calm mode.

Now I breathe deeply, letting my belly hang out as often as possible. I have learned to breathe into my emotions instead of holding in my muscles to suppress emotions. Whenever I need to get in touch with my emotions I take ten very slow, even, deep breaths. I take each breath to the count of at least four inhaling and the count of four exhaling, the slower the better. This is called the "Oxygen Cocktail" or "O Cocktail." Whenever I need a break from work, I take an O Cocktail. Whenever I encounter an irritating person, I share an O Cocktail with them. Whenever I need to make that difficult phone call, I have an O Cocktail first. Whenever I can't sleep, I order soothing and nurturing O Cocktails. What I used to do when I took a break was snack. Now whenever I need a break, a real break, I breathe in this manner for five minutes. The wonderful thing is that if you do this while you are in rush-hour traffic, the traffic will not cause stress. Breathing is healing because it is the ultimate way of truly being with ourselves.

exercise:

To obtain the benefits of this exercise you must acquire a small book of blank pages, something in a reasonable size that you can carry with you at all times. This book will serve as your eating journal and your emotional journal. It will serve as the registry of your journey as you master the process of getting in touch with your emotions. It will also be used to record resistance to any of our exercises. Remember, you are not reading this book simply to gain insight. You have not embarked on a journey of merely knowledge. You are committed to a personal transformation that will end emotional hunger.

1. Each morning for the first three months of the transformation, create a realistic, healthy eating plan for the day. Breathe into the intention of this eating plan and into whatever emotional discomfort arises.

2. Before each meal, take three to five minutes of cleansing breaths and observe the emotions that come up. Sit with any discomfort or anxiety and really process these emotions before eating. You will be surprised at how this one simple step will help you to be present and to eat calmly and intentionally.

3. When you get home, take 10 cleansing breaths. Ask with healing intention, "What would fulfill my need for feeling relaxed, comfortable and truly at home?" Follow your inner guidance and embrace the comfort of your home.

breathing to shift emotional hunger

Situations will arise when you experience hunger and you know that there is no physical justification. Here is a powerful process to get to the imbalance that is fueling the emotional hunger. (You can print it from our web site www.emotionalhunger.com and keep it in your wallet or purse for when you need it).

- Breathe deeply and smoothly.
- Bring oxygen into your lower abdomen until it is full. Feel the healing power as your chest naturally expands.
- Allow every single muscle in your body to relax.
- Relax profoundly and breathe deeply.
- Be with your breath and watch as your belly expands.
- Feel the healing sensation within your body.
- Come into the power of being completely alive. Be in the now.
- Be present in the moment by feeling all the sensations of your body.
- In the now, there are no regrets, there are no plans for the future, no agendas for what this breathing experience will achieve. There is only you and your breath.
- Allow the here and now to be your entire universe. In the now all healing happens.
- Allow the gift of peace to reside within you while you remain wholly present in the moment.
- There is no past, there is no future. There is only the fulfillment of being now.
- Relax and breathe deeply as your belly expands and brings the life force into every single cell of your being.
- Be with your body and let it be a pillow of relaxation and genuine peace.
- Breathe consciously, deeply, fully and evenly, and experience total comfort within your body. Surrender to complete peace.
- Experience the breath as it expands your belly and carries all the toxins from your body.

- There is no striving or agenda, there is only your search for clarity accompanied by deep, slow, conscious breathing and the power of now.
- Breathe smoothly and deeply and allow yourself to be cradled in the arms of nature as you reach complete relaxation. Open to the wisdom of your body and the guidance of your inner being.
- Keep breathing in this manner until you are utterly and totally relaxed. Every single muscle is completely relaxed; the muscles in your forehead, your eyelids, your cheeks and your lips are totally and completely relaxed.
- Finally, as you continue breathing deeply, ask your subconscious, "What is the issue? What is bothering me? What is out of balance? What do I need?"

yoga

"Once we accept our limits, we go beyond them."

- Brendan Francis

For many emotional eaters, having clarity and access to our emotions is an elusive proposition. Compulsive overeating, like any addiction, is a manifestation of one or two factors:

1. Not having access to our emotions,
2. Not being able to be with our emotions.

If we don't have access to our emotions, we will not recognize or express what we are feeling. When we binge, we might understand that something is wrong, that there is an emotional imbalance. Yet we don't feel the emotions directly with the clarity and intensity we experience when we sit quietly, when we are directly in touch with them. Experiencing emotion as hunger is not accessing the emotion. We have either learned to suppress our emotions, or our energy centers are so out of balance that there is no clarity to our feelings. Our goal is to have unobstructed access to our emotions – to be able to feel, be, and express "I'm lonely," "I'm frustrated," "I'm disappointed," "I'm devastated," "I'm angry," and to experience these emotions directly with our entire body. We are choosing to feel all of these emotions instead of confusing them with physical hunger.

Because our emotions are stored in our bodies as energies, it is critical to have the body's energy centers and energy conduits balanced, open

chapter 4: tools for the journey

and flowing. The openness and fluidity of our bodies' emotional energies allow us to have access to our emotions. In the case of buried emotional trauma, we also need a means to release these repressed energies. Yoga, in my personal experience and in the opinion of many experts, is one of the most effective means of clearing the energy channels, which allow our emotions to flow freely.

There are at least 16 million Americans who practice yoga on a regular basis. Most practice it because they consider yoga the best investment of their time, others because of yoga's many healing benefits such as curing arthritis, loosening stiffness, or restoring muscle tone. Others simply do it because yoga makes them feel better. If you have never tried yoga, or if you have a preconception of what yoga is, please read this section with an open mind. We are going to illustrate – not teach – specific yoga postures that can be used to balance five of the energy centers, or chakras. When these chakras are out of balance they affect our ability to deal with emotional hunger because we don't have access to the energy of our emotions.

For yoga postures to be effective, they must be executed with focus and intent while simultaneously moving and stretching the specific areas of the body to open and release emotional blockage or imbalance. This release can come in a variety of ways: a flood of strong emotions, memories, or a physical sensation. We need to be fully present to get the many benefits of our practice. It would be advantageous to wear, look at, or have in your vicinity the color of the energy center that you are working on. Imagine the center opening like a camera aperture, flower bud or trap door, and the energy flooding every cell of the hips, legs and feet. By sustaining the image clearly while holding the pertinent yoga posture, and by working with your breath, the agent of the life force becomes available. Yoga, when practiced with awareness, has the ability to infuse the practitioner with positive qualities unique to each posture.

Yoga is an advanced contemplative practice, and no extraneous effort should be involved. In other words, you should not strain to conform to a mental image of the posture. Do what you can and breathe, because each deep, even breath is a reflection of balance and calmness. Whenever you are experiencing shortness of breath or shallow, uneven breathing, you are not getting the benefits of the posture. Deep, slow breathing is essential, allowing the movement to follow the breath and draw you inward.

Please note that the illustrations of yoga postures included in this book are not meant to be instructional, nor do they provide a comprehensive description of how to do them at home. As a matter of fact, the range of motion depicted in many of the yoga pictures cannot be achieved for several weeks until the supporting muscles are re-awakened or strengthened. Instead, these pictures are included to illustrate yoga's accessibility and to give you an idea of what kind of investment it would take to keep these energy centers open and flowing. If you choose yoga as a means of getting in touch with your emotions, you should attend classes at a local yoga studio that promotes emotional healing as one of its goals. Many yoga instructors understand the benefits of yoga but do not necessarily have a class that specifically addresses emotional healing. If that is the case in your area, you might want to discuss this chapter of the book with an experienced yoga teacher who has some understanding of the goals of these postures as they relate to emotional healing. Ask the yoga teacher if he or she can work with you one on one, or if there is a class that would closely meet your needs. Alternatively, you can visit our website at www.emotionalhunger.com to find out if there are any yoga studios near you that promotes emotional healing.

One last point before we illustrate the healing yoga postures. It is critical not to confuse bodywork such as yoga with exercising. Exercising is wonderful to tone the body, increase aerobic capacity, lower blood pressure, increase the lean muscle-to-fat ratio, release endorphins, change our mood, improve our vitality, and help with our weight-loss objectives. There are even some yoga practices, such as hot yoga, that have a very strong aerobic component. However, exercising is not bodywork. Bodywork is a therapy that can help release suppressed emotions stored in our tissues and can teach us how to access the emotions we hold in our bodies.

building blocks

The energy centers are building blocks for each other. When is balanced and flows freely, it reinforces and helps the other centers to develop. As Maslow expressed in his hierarchy of needs, one does not seek expression and creativity on an empty stomach. Likewise one cannot achieve love of self if our primary emotion is insecurity. We cannot genuinely love and accept others if we are plagued with fear and anxiety. As we address the issues that cause emotional eating, we will experience the positive influence of personal growth through our emotional, physical and spiritual lives.

Maslow's Hierarchy of Needs

survival center – emotional issues

Let's begin with the root chakra, the survival center, located at the base of the spine, between the perineum and the coccyx. This chakra corresponds to our most basic needs surrounding survival, food, shelter, warmth, etc. This is the center where fears and general anxieties are experienced. If you are insecure, if you are the type of person that lives in constant fear of what could go wrong, if you internalize the news media reports, if you are generally anxious or paranoid and food is what makes you feel safe and secure in the world, then your Survival Center is blocked or out of balance. When this center is flowing freely, we have access to our survival resources and we can begin healing whatever it is that makes us feel unsafe and insecure in the world.

The survival center also influences our social identity and the values we adopt from external groups with whom we associate, be they religious, racial or political. It is the tribal mindset – what we embrace as our "truth." The immediate family to which we were born forms our fundamental values around the survival center; balancing this chakra facilitates the healing of family injuries. This center nourishes our lower hip area, legs and feet.

Often our words betray our emotional imbalances, shedding light on which energy centers process our feelings. Some of the language that lets us know our survival center is the starting point for our emotions: "getting on my feet again," "he's a real pain in the ass," "I got swept off my feet," "I'm feeling stuck," and "I'm putting my foot down." Listening carefully to your recurring phrases and being aware of your most frequent emotions will give you clues to begin investigating your own emotional healing through yoga.

Opening and balancing the survival center will help you stop overeating if some of your emotional hunger is fueled by any of the feelings of insecurity, fear, belonging, or having fuzzy personal boundaries. Yoga postures that help activate and clear the survival center facilitate our ability to feel emotions that emanate from this center. Once again, it is not my intention to teach in detail how to do the yoga postures; these illustrations are included only to give you an idea of the commitment required if you choose yoga for body work. These postures should NOT be performed without initial supervision by a trained yoga instructor.

The Chair

The chair pose cultivates a sense of being settled, stability and trust. One can discharge negativity through the feet.

Dilia De La Altagracia

The Triangle

The Triangle encourages
balance between heaven and
earth, ideals and reality. It
extends the lines of energy
through the limbs in three
directions.

The Tree

The Tree encourages
and helps us extend
our roots, creating a
calm, centered mind.
Balancing postures
generally encourage
one to extend
energetic roots and
are particularly
grounding and
centering.
Balancing highlights
the parts that the
mind and breath play
in our lives.
Try balancing after
you've had any
negative interactions
and you will see
what I mean.

sensation center – emotional issues

The sensation center is the second chakra and it is located at the level of our sexual organs. It governs all cravings (including food, cigarettes, alcohol and drugs), compulsiveness, sexual desire, frustration, violation, inhibition, revulsion; desires for touch, or stimulation and the physical sensations that frustration may bring up. Clearly the sensation center deals with many of the aspects of emotional overeating, specifically food cravings and compulsions. While the survival center governs familial or tribal group relationships, the sensation center also governs the relationships with individuals – you and your boss, child, spouse, parent, and any other one-on-one relationship. To discover if this center's energies are blocked, we can ask ourselves: How balanced are our various one-on-one relationships? What unresolved one-on-one issues do we have?

Also stored within this center are issues of control and blame, guilt and shame, possessions and finances, and addictions. Some of the language that points to imbalance in the sensation center are our constant expressions of hunger and phrases such as, "that really turns me on," "f— you!" "thinking with your zipper," or "being led by your hormones." By paying close attention to what we are thinking and saying, we can begin to identify imbalance or blockage within this energy center.

The Mantra for Life, "go with the flow," comes from the sensation center. Repeat this meditatively while practicing yoga and throughout the day. We sometimes try to hang on and control our lives so desperately that we forget we can control very little. Worry begins in the sensation center. When you find yourself worrying and trying to control circumstances or people, try going with the flow. This means acceptance of where you are, where others are, and that there is a "bigger picture." This is a simple concept, but one that is difficult to experience in our everyday lives.

Besides yoga, other movements that will get the sensation center's energy flowing are belly dancing and Latin dancing, where you can truly move those hips. Let go and have fun! When working on the sensation center, wear or look at the color orange. Listen to water sounds and music. Meditate and practice yoga postures by a bubbling stream or gentle ocean surf. The sensation center's energy is the water element. Flow, don't stagnate.

chapter 4: tools for the journey

Several yoga postures that help get the flow activated in the sensation center follow. These can all be practiced as movements or held postures. Practicing them in a movement series will enhance the water element of the second chakra. Focus on the pelvic area, and gently hold a specific issue in your consciousness as you practice, dedicating the entire time of practice to that issue. Notice what comes up for you in terms of feelings, memories, sensations or insights.

Standing forward bends create a link between first and second chakras. Your focus and intent in one chakra can also bring balance to the neighboring area on which you are working.

Standing Forward Bend Wide

The Standing Forward
Bend Wide calms the
brain and helps relieve
stress and mild
depression. It also
reduces fatigue and
anxiety.

Sitting Forward Bend

Kneeling Lunge

Pelvic Roll

power center – emotional issues

The third chakra is the power center located at the pit of the stomach. It is where emotions such as anger and feelings of lack are processed. It provides sensations to the body that work as intuitive functions. The clues in our colloquial language serve as further evidence: "I had this gut feeling," "I felt like I was kicked in the stomach," "I had butterflies in my stomach," "I had the wind knocked out of me," "It was a gut wrenching experience," or we say someone "has guts" or is "gutsy."

The power center can act as our personal warning system. When we are not being true to ourselves, or are associating with those who may compromise our integrity, we may get a "funny feeling" in the power center. This energy center governs our self-image. Energetically, it reflects our relationship with ourselves. With a balanced power center, we make good decisions, have the courage to take risks and have the ability to generate action and handle crises. The power center is the seat of our integrity, our ability to give and then keep our word. We "walk

chapter 4: tools for the journey

our talk" through a strong, balanced power center and develop into spiritual warriors rather than becoming angry and malicious. We see these distortions readily in our society in people who impose their will, beliefs and way of life on others. Force is distorted power-center energy. The Chinese call it the Yang without the balance of Yin.

When power-center energy is distorted, we may lack the ability to trust our instincts, be overly sensitive to criticism from others, or lack a sense of personal honor. Many compulsive overeaters reflect self-loathing and an extreme lack of self-confidence.

Yellow is the color of the power center. In our culture, yellow is a sign of cowardice, exemplified by the sayings "yellow belly" and "yellow streak down his back." In some unconscious way, we are aware of this connection, but we have it skewed. A yellow belly denotes strong power center energy – someone who can stand up for what he believes. Contrary to our Western ideal, an Eastern concept of the belly is that it should be soft and malleable. Are our abdomens rigid? How about our belief systems? Are we wishy-washy? Are we open to new thought, new concepts, new ideas about our views and our place in the world? What are our passions in life? The therapeutic connection with the power center and yoga practice is the intent first, and then the practice of postures or movement series that activate this area of the body.

The Bridge

The Cat

chapter 4: tools for the journey

laughter

The ability to laugh fully and joyfully is associated with a balanced power center. This simple practice has been credited with increased immune response and stress reduction. Patch Adams, M.D., has been a proponent of laughter as healing practice for many years. Norman Cousins is also well known for his work in this area. How often do we allow ourselves a deep belly laugh? We are so tight that we usually chuckle high in a restricted chest. Next time something tickles you really let go and laugh. Reclaim your passion for living!

heart center – emotional issues

All emotions related to unworthiness and grief are processed in the heart center. The heart center marks a transition point on our spiritual path. It comes midway between our more physical, mundane life and our higher spiritual evolution, and it links them. The heart imbues our everyday lives with compassion, which opens us to love on all levels. The first, most important level is love of self, because if we do not love ourselves we will not find balanced, healthy love coming toward or flowing from us – there will always be conditions or strings attached.

The heart chakra resides in the center of the chest. You will have felt its energetic presence as a physical sensation if you've ever had a "broken heart" or expanded in empathic compassion for someone. The clues in our colloquial language that point to heart chakra involvement are: "It pulled at my heart strings," "felt like I was stabbed in the back," "have a heart," and "get off my back." We say we are "green with envy" when our hearts slam shut with this emotion. The traditional color of the heart chakra, coincidentally, is a beautiful emerald green, the core of which is pink. The element of this center is air, and we may experience shortness of breath when encountering someone who "smothers us with affection" or "takes our breath away."

When the heart center is out of balance our compassion is compromised. We experience a selfish passion that is manifested as differences between ourselves and other rather than our similarities. Through the heart center, we breathe freely and fully, opening to selflessness – a step further on our development as spiritual beings. Many of my yoga teachers end the practice with the word "Namasté," which means the Divine in me recognizes the Divine in you.

Dilia De La Altagracia

The heart center opens us to subtler dimensions of perception and experience. Necessary to a healthy heart center, however, is a balance of the survival, sensation, and power centers. Without this vital balance, we have intellectual understanding without empathy, lust masquerading as love, and high ideals without the ability to carry those ideals into our own lives practically.

The Christian mystical tradition honors the sacred hearts of Jesus and Mary as the source of divine forgiveness. This shows us the path for our own full healing. Forgiveness is not condoning or forgetting the wrongs done to us, but letting them go. We grow. But without letting go and forgiving, the events eat at us constantly, causing pain, anguish and disease. We shut our hearts and live in the past.

Working with the breath is an excellent way to get the heart center energy moving. Emotions may bubble up to the surface when least expected. Allow the movement of emotion to follow the breath outward. Don't cling to or push away the emotion or the event behind it. Observe that as the breath moves through you, so can the emotional charge – feel the anger, let the tears flow, experience the fear, work through the grief but remain in the present moment where true healing is experienced. Your breath will help you do this!

It is fascinating that the shoulders, chest and upper back are typically the first muscles to stiffen as we grow up. Most of us have a lot of heart pain. To the Buddhists opening the heart chakra is a prerequisite to being truly alive and compassionate humans. We grow, it seems, through transcending difficulties.

Some postures that will help you discover your heart energies follow.

The Camel

sitting rotation poses

In the next couple of pages we depict a few variations of sitting rotations poses. While holding these poses we are directed to relax our shoulders, our hands are used as anchors to stabilize us longer. We then breathe deeply, expanding the chest cavity. As we move into these rotations, the energy is gently squeezed upward, expanding the heart. If you feel a release we are directed to gently turn farther.

Dilia De La Altagracia

Sitting Twist (Front View)

Sitting Twist (Back View)

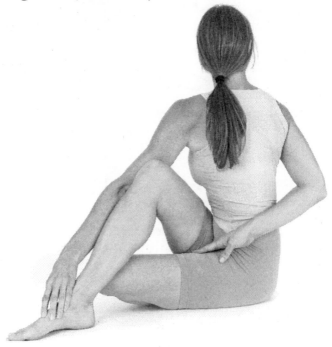

The Upward Dog

The Head of the Cow

Dilia De La Altagracia

The Pigeon

chapter 4: tools for the journey

creative center – emotional issues

"In the beginning was the Sound, and the Sound was with God, and the Sound was God" (The original Greek word "logos" was translated as word, but also means sound.) In yogic philosophy, that sound was OM, the point of creation, the stirring of spirit to know itself. The fifth chakra is located on the neck and it is the creative center where the emotional impetus to create originates. It opens to the front and back and corresponds to the thyroid and parathyroid glands of the endocrine system. The creative center is the element of ether/space, and its color is blue.

Many emotional overeaters, particularly women, have self-expression issues. We are not encouraged to express how we feel, what we want or how we want it. "No" is a very difficult word for us, hence the packed schedule with no time for ourselves and the inability to say no to demands or situations that are not in our best interest.

Clues in the colloquial language that may point to creative center issues are "so-and-so is a pain in the neck," "talking till I'm blue in the face," "bite your tongue," "I'm sticking my neck out," and "so angry I could spit." If we don't express grief or gratitude, we can feel it as an unexpressed "lump in the throat." Perhaps we chronically "clear" our throats or find we have a "frog" in the throat. A chronic sore throat can be an indication of creative center energy imbalance. Those who are presently in their seventies and eighties grew up in a time when tonsillectomies were the norm. It is interesting to note that it seemed very important for this group to keep the status quo by not asking questions or voicing a different opinion. It was a generation that happily "followed the leader" unlike those that grew up in the 1960s.

There is great hesitancy in many people to make sounds, especially in front of others. The manifestations of the creative center are speaking our truth, listening, hearing and being heard. Being judgmental and sharing personal experiences are creative center issues. Toning and chanting are helpful to balancing and opening the creative center, do not underestimate their power. Practice alone until you gain confidence. Robert Gass in his book *Chanting: Discovering Spirit in Sound*[6], says, "Chant is more than a repetitive song – it is an extraordinary way to integrate breath, heartbeat, emotion and purpose bringing increased blood flow to the head, balancing the brain waves and inspiring the singer as well as the listener." The postures below focus on the creative center, or throat chakra.

Shoulder Stand

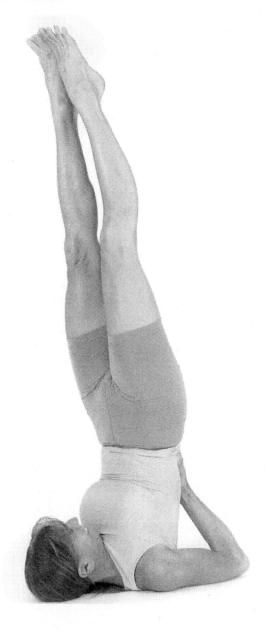

chapter 4: tools for the journey

Pose of Tranquility

The Baby Squirrel

The Plough

The Fish Pose

chapter 4: tools for the journey

alternatives to yoga

If you find yourself completely averse to attempting yoga, be assured that it is not the only means of achieving consistent and clear access to your emotions. I've summarized some other bodywork alternatives in Appendix B. We will also maintain a list of alternative bodywork healing practices on our website, www.emotionalhunger.com.

meditation

Healing breathing and yoga were instrumental in helping me remove the blocks that impeded access to my emotions. For my new emotional flexibility along with countless other physical benefits, I will continue to practice yoga. For the first time in my life, I am in touch with my emotions, and I am able to verbalize my feelings.

However, there is a huge distinction between having awareness of and access to our emotions and being able to be with our emotions until they dissipate. Yes, I'm now able to differentiate between boredom and loneliness, disappointment and anger. But it is meditation that has allowed me to be with my emotions. Why is that?

Until the mind is tranquil, it is the self-appointed king of problem solving, the central switchboard of all processing – the Grand Central Station where all emotional discomfort first registers. When the mind is in control, it attempts to process our emotions, and it disrupts our ability to sit with those emotions. First, it interprets emotions that emanate from our bodies as discomfort, and because we have convinced ourselves that we are not allowed to experience any discomfort, the mind finds a way of dealing with that discomfort – in our case by projecting the illusion that food will spare us. I finally understood why my mind couldn't conquer this addiction: It had never occurred to me that my mind was the very mechanism that was interfering with my ability to get in touch with my emotions.

For those of us who value our intelligence highly, the notion that the mind must be quieted creates an internal battle. The chatter of the mind not only interferes with our ability to be with our emotions, but in its role of problem solver it misidentifies our emotional needs as hunger.

The core of every addiction is our inability to be with ourselves. The moment there is no distraction, no social protocol, no demands, no background noise, just the bare essence of self, emotional hunger manifests in full strength. This hunger is the mechanism by which we run away from the discomfort of being alone. We are so conditioned to avoid this state that when it does occur we become inexplicably hungry. That's why for many of us hunger starts at the end of a lovely evening. We have said goodbye to friends, we have retrieved the car, we are driving away. We are alone. That's when we begin to think about what we are going to eat when we get home.

Many times we can't even wait to get home, and we start salivating as we drive past each fast food place. We are so uncomfortable when left by ourselves, bared, exposed, unencumbered with titles, tasks, responsibilities, or entertainment, that when it does happen our retreat from this foreign state of being is food.

For the Western mind, meditation is very difficult in the beginning. We have been conditioned to multitask – to cope with stressful situations, to have a full plate – and we are accustomed to having some level of noise in our lives. The concept of sitting without TV, radio or any other form of external stimulus, embracing silence and clearing our minds for fifteen to twenty minutes seems like insanity. I fought meditation with every possible excuse in my intellectual arsenal.

I experienced three stages while trying to integrate meditation into my life – avoidance, thinking about it, and making every possible excuse why I couldn't do it today. It occurred to me that if the mind is what we use to schedule our day, it will not agree willingly to shut down for fifteen or twenty minutes. There was never time to meditate – at least that was my perception, and that perception was a destructive illusion that kept me overeating compulsively. During the first three weeks that I started meditating consistently, my mind kept screaming "I'M BORED" in an effort to return to the familiar occupation of non-stop busyness. But as I learned, boredom is the way to mask suppressed feelings and sabotage their processing. Therefore, transcending boredom is the entry to wonderful and life-altering work. The challenge is to be undeterred by the boredom and to stay with meditation until the suppressed feelings unveil themselves.

Through sheer willpower, which in this case proved helpful, I began reluctantly. At first I had to force myself to meditate. Eventually however, feeling its benefit, I surrendered to the meditation and began needing it in my life. Meditation helped when I was tired but needed to work. Meditation also unveiled creativity as well as problem-solving

chapter 4: tools for the journey

insights. More importantly, meditation helped me stay binge-free and awake to my tendencies toward overeating.

When you first attempt meditating, try it for five minutes a day during the first week. Then the second week for ten minutes, then fifteen, then twenty, then twenty minutes twice a day. True growth is a gradual process. Be prepared to sit with the underlying noise and chaos of your life, of your mind. Be prepared to watch yourself make every possible excuse to avoid meditation.

Let me repeat that the number one excuse for not meditating is not having time. Here you have to take into your soul the truth of what keeps you addicted. Do you have time to be FAT? How many extra minutes every day do you spend feeding that addiction? How much longer does it take to get dressed in the morning because of excess weight? Have you ever tried to put on panty hose when you are eighty pounds overweight? How many times do you forget where the car keys are because of the frantic pace of life? How much time do you spend hating yourself for being overweight? The time excuse is just that – an excuse.
When we really want something, we find a way to get to it. Meditation is not sexy. It is not instant gratification, and it isn't in vogue. It is, however, one of the most powerful tools we can employ in our quest to live binge-free.

One of the main reasons given for the effectiveness of meditation has to do with the way we usually spend our time. During the day we are constantly subjected to sensory input, and our minds are always active. We read from the computer and newspapers, we study books, write reports, have conversations and solve problems. Typically, as we do these normal activities, we engage in a constant mental commentary, sort of an inner "Drama of Me." Usually people aren't fully aware of their background mental activity. Meditation allows this chatter to subside and usually results in the mind becoming peaceful, calm and focused. In essence, meditation allows our awareness to become rejuvenated.

How is meditation different from relaxation? Relaxation is a common by-product of meditation. Relaxation itself can assume many other forms from taking a hot bath to reclining in the La-Z-Boy™ watching TV. Meditation is an active process in which the meditator remains fully cognizant and aware. It also attempts to transcend the thought process whereas many forms of relaxation still engage the mind.

Meditation allows the body to relax and can offset the effects of stress, both mental and physical, to a much greater degree than passive relaxation. Many people become interested in meditation because it helps lower their stress level, and it helps them sleep better. But the benefits go far beyond relaxation. For me, meditation mitigated anxiety, one of the main motives for overeating. There is no such thing as a calm and harmonious binge, and meditation calms the frantic mind.

Calmness and presence of mind are qualities that we experience when we are fully aware of our choices. Meditative calmness and presence of mind bring deeper consciousness and mitigate anxiety. When we meditate, the unfocused consciousness and frenetic energy necessary to a good binge are eradicated

Anxiety is a major component of other emotions that lead to overeating. Insomnia, for example. When the mind is quiet, most people can experience restful sleep and minimize the occurrence of fatigue due to lack of sleep. Tiredness leads to overeating. Absence of anxiety leads to that sacred no, when we say no to overeating, when we begin to experience self-love. We are anxious when we are faced with the desire to overeat. Meditation affords us the serenity to contemplate and contrast the pleasure of eating that second piece of lasagna with the pleasure of feeling vital and not weighed down by a full stomach.

western medicine and meditation

In his book *Meditation as Medicine*[7], Dharma Singh Khalsa M.D. states that long-term meditators experience 80% fewer incidents of heart disease and 50% fewer incidents of cancer than non-meditators. Dr. Singh Khasa references several studies that corroborate these statements.

According to Dr. Herbert Benson, founder of the Mind/Body Medical Institute at Boston's New England Deaconess Hospital, meditation can be an important complement to conventional medical treatment for depression, anxiety, hypertension, cardiac arrhythmia, migraine headaches, irritable bowel syndrome, insomnia and many other conditions. The relaxation response technique pioneered by Dr. Benson has been used to reduce the side effects of chemotherapy, minimize postoperative pain, alleviate symptoms of premenstrual syndrome and even treat infertility.

chapter 4: tools for the journey

One New England Deaconess study of a group of patients suffering chronic pain reported a 36% reduction in visits to their managed care facility in the two years following completion of the Institute's mind/body program. The group, which combined meditation with other self-care strategies such as nutrition, exercise and psychotherapy, reported milder symptoms and less anxiety and depression after completion of the program.

Dr. Benson, author of *The Relaxation Response*[8], one of the first reports by a Western physician on the nature and benefits of meditation, has documented the uniquely altered quality of the meditative state. Not like sleeping and not like being fully awake, deep meditation is characterized by distinct, positive changes in metabolism, heart rate, respiration, blood pressure, and brain chemistry. When you consider that an estimated 60% to 90% of all doctor's office visits may be stress related, the benefits of meditation become obvious. Under stress, there is increased sympathetic nervous system activity and elevated blood pressure, heart rate, and respiration. Circulation changes, and blood moves away from the periphery into muscles and vital organs. This is why a person often looks pale when stressed.

To meditate properly, you must make an appointment with yourself on a regular basis. I recommend at least three times a week. Others say daily, but I've found three times weekly works best for me as a minimum. As you grow more deeply in touch with your needs, you will be able to judge this for yourself. Your meditation time must be at a time of day when interruptions are least likely, and I also recommend that you turn the ringers on your telephones off and program your answering machine before you begin your meditation. Remember, this is your special time to be with your true self. Hang a "Do Not Disturb" sign on the door, if you like, prior to beginning your meditation. I usually pick a time when I know that my son will be out of the house.

If you need additional guidance on how to meditate, I've included a summary in Appendix A. Several resources that provide training or sell products on the topic of meditation are listed on my website at www.emotionalhunger.com.

more on benefits of meditation

- Meditation will afford you the gift of remaining present and calm in any situation. Calmness and awareness are the keys to avoiding overeating.
- It encourages deeper understanding of yourself and others. It will enable you to be with your emotions. It will be easier for you to stand up for yourself and, therefore, your relationships with others will improve.
- Meditation will teach you about true enjoyment. As a result, you will gradually stop injuring yourself with gluttony. You will stop imagining that the pain of overeating is pleasure.
- It is an effective way to become friends with stress, be with it, and use it for your benefit.
- Most diseases stem from the discord between mind and body. Meditation will bring your body, mind, emotions and spirit – all of the many facets of human existence – into harmony.
- Meditation teaches us is that our home – our beautiful universe – is impermanent by its very nature. You will begin to understand, appreciate and make peace with the passing events in the world.

be with your emotions

"What you choose not to look at in your life rules your life."
– Lynn Andrews

- Do not look for distraction.
- Do not go to the mall.
- Do not take a bubble bath.
- Do not call a friend.
- Do not…run away from your emotions

Sit with your emotions

How, then, can we stop emotional hunger? By being consciously with our emotions. Being with our emotions is not about coping, it is about being. Being with our emotions is not about finding alternatives, it is about feeling.

For many years I had read that it was only necessary to learn what to do whenever I felt emotional hunger. If I was lonely, I was supposed to

chapter 4: tools for the journey

call a friend. If I was bored I was supposed to find an interesting activity. If I was angry I was supposed to express my anger in an "I am" statement.

The mainstream prescription is to be a human doing, but the emotional hunger ends when we are willing to be a human being. A famous quote by Carl Jung says "What you resist persists." Whatever you are resisting must be embraced. Let your emotions burn through the discomfort. Let go of expectations and resistance.

The prescription "find something to do" is not in your best interest when you are an emotional eater. It doesn't teach the most basic and important of all human skills: to be with ourselves. We don't know how to sit with our emotions because we don't want to experience discomfort. Yet our pain, our disappointment, our anguish, our fear are the most transformational opportunities presented to us.

Fear of pain is detrimental. Fear of pain is ineffective. It actually amplifies pain. Fear is a powerful catalyst that in fact adds more energy whatever emotion we are suppressing. Paradoxically, by resisting our genuine emotions we experience more pain. It is the difference between getting an injection when we are relaxed and having the same injection when we are tense.

Pain is transformational; the willingness to be with the pain of our emotions is the key to stopping overeating. By avoiding our pain, we are also avoiding our lives. We have lived that approach, and look at the results. I tried it for years. I carried eighty extra pounds of avoidance because I bought into the delusion that I should never, under any circumstances, experience any discomfort.

Sitting with our emotions means there is no resistance to any of our feelings.

The Zen masters say that one must go into the belly of the beast and sit there until the beast devours you. Ending emotional overeating is not a journey for those who are still seduced by gimmicks that promise you will be thin and blissful in a few weeks. This is a journey about experiencing all the disappointment of the empty promises and blaming ourselves for their failure. This is a journey about surrendering to being with our emotions, about finally being willing to be with ourselves.

Dilia De La Altagracia

Franklin Delano Roosevelt once said that there is nothing to fear but fear itself. Part of the process of confronting emotions is to understand that by trying to avoid discomfort we amplify our emotions and grow them into disproportionate monsters. Naturally thin people also get sad, disappointed, lonely and bored. The difference is that they don't eat to avoid discomfort. Thin people either have a different addiction they use to deal with these emotions – smoking, for example – or they face emotions as they happen. We simply must surrender to the pain within the emotion. Resistance is counterproductive and as we've experienced, ineffective.

The first breakthrough, and it's a critical one, is to accept discomfort without battle, blocking, defiance, negotiation, obstruction or refusal. Drop the resistance and open your arms wide. Just sit and say, "Here I am." The second, difficult breakthrough, is to stay with the discomfort until your body experiences a shift, until you feel that the emotion has been fully experienced, fully dissipated and that there is no energy left in it.

How do we know when that happens? When the hunger disappears. By expending the fuel that feeds the hunger, the hunger goes away. The first hundred times I was willing to face the discomfort of my emotions, I experienced anxiety and even mild depression. Whatever was lurking and masking itself as hunger was not going away without a fight. Keep in mind that our socialization has taught us to avoid discomfort at any cost. There was always a way around the discomfort. For most of us the notion that we have to be present, truly and non-judgmentally, with uncomfortable emotions, emotions we have managed to eat through for many years, is second only to having a root canal without anesthesia. Be prepared for this resistance; be ready for the surge of anxiety. Otherwise, you will give up and begin searching for the next miracle diet in this month's popular magazine.

My reaction was to become so anxious that I wanted out. I wanted to run to the comfort of food. Breathing into the anxiety became a critical aid. The most I could do in the beginning was to simply be with the anxiety. As I made progress and realized that it was not going to kill me, I began the process of being with my emotions.

Then, in my typical approach to life, I asked, "What else can I do to make this better?" I made a project plan for what seemed the optimal time to learn to sit with my emotions. Then I thought, "Okay, I sit with my emotions, I stop overeating, I lose weight, I look beautiful, I find a

chapter 4: tools for the journey

nice soul mate and I live happily ever after. Why didn't anyone tell me that was all I had to do? Damn, it would have saved me a lot of aggravation and time!"

But it isn't that easy. Once I started sitting with my emotions, I had to let go of expectations, payoffs, goals, objectives and time frames for when the weight would come off. When I began bargaining with loneliness, loneliness did not dissipate. I was once again just playing a head game, an intellectual tit for tat. That is not what sitting with emotions is about. I found that the more I tried to finish the process of being with my emotions, the longer it took. When I truly let go without an agenda or time frame, I saw real progress and the catharsis began.

All my life I had been trained to "do" – the profound sense of inadequacy always asked "what am I supposed to do?" As I progressed, I began plotting again. "OK, I've got it. How can I feel the loneliness more intensely, so that it will go quicker? How can I embrace the disappointment more profoundly so I can arrive at my destination of blissful thinness quicker?" One of the subtleties that kept eluding me was that I just had to sit, I just had to be with my emotions. I didn't have to analyze, I didn't have to comprehend, I didn't have to force.

The delicate concept of being in the moment began to crystallize. This goes beyond the Zen concept as popularly understood. It is quieting our busy minds, that is the key to experiencing our emotions. Just being here now – totally, completely, without projections, without regrets, without the never-ending list of things that need to be done – clears the path to what we are feeling before it masks itself as emotional hunger. When I experienced my unencumbered emotions and sat with them until they dissipated, I felt the light bulb had finally come on! I understood that spending so much useless energy regretting the past and worrying about the future interfered with my ability to feel. I understood that if I didn't learn how I felt, I would end up eating the illusion. It became very important to be present in the moment. Not because it was some cool Zen concept, but because learning to be in the moment would contribute to ending my overeating addiction.

I devised an exercise to employ whenever the old voices in my head began their torture. My mantra became:

> "All of my needs are being met right now."
> "All of my needs are being met right now."
> "All of my needs are being met right now."

True physical hunger is not selective. When you are really hungry, most anything will do. Your stomach makes noises, your blood sugar level drops drastically, you experience a sense of instability, and your taste and olfactory senses are awakened. In contrast emotional hunger craves very specific foods and is not accompanied by any of these physical symptoms. Once I felt the distinction between physical and emotional hunger, I finally accepted that the first sensation for most of my suppressed emotions would manifest itself as emotional hunger. I began to welcome emotional hunger as the knock on the door that let me know I needed to go inside and find out the trigger. I have learned that whenever I'm hungry, and it is not physical, I need to be with whatever is fueling my emotional hunger, to watch it, to accept it, to embrace the physical sensations and to be with the discomfort without resistance, judgment, alternatives, or detour. When I accept and truly experience the feelings behind my emotional hunger, it stops.

For those who have never experienced emotional hunger, the concept of "willpower" always arises as the obvious solution. During the process of writing this book, one of the professionals I met was a well toned, Jack LaLanne body. We briefly discussed the book, and he told me what a great thing I had done in writing it. "Yes!" he exclaimed. "I couldn't agree more. All people need to do is learn willpower." He had read the book, but his lack of understanding of emotional hunger had led him to miss my message and see only his own dedication to willpower, a message I had heard many times, a message that does grave disservice to emotional eaters.

Being with our emotions is not about "willpower." Resisting the urge to eat always led me to give in to the hunger. When I resisted the hunger, I strengthened it by feeding it additional energy. Accepting and experiencing the discomfort, without getting up and running to the refrigerator, helped to dissipate it.

accepting all our emotions

When I first thought I understood what I needed to experience, I was euphoric. "OK, I got it. I have to love myself and accept my emotions. I have to sit with my emotions until they dissipate. I have to love my body and accept it as an intelligent source of wisdom." It was not that easy.

chapter 4: tools for the journey

An additional challenge met while sitting with my emotions began when I started to reject any feelings I thought were contrary to self-love: disapproval, resentment or disappointment. I was determined to feel self-love because I understood it to be was an important aspect of recovery. The paradox was to accept that even my feelings of rejection were genuinely my feelings – they still emanated from my soul. I had to accept them. Only by embracing all of my feelings, even those mislabeled "self-rejecting," I began to accept myself totally.

The entire physical universe is made up of opposite but balancing energies. The perfect example to illustrate this concept is matter. All matter in the cosmos is made up of atoms. All atoms are made of negative and positive charges, opposing forces that balance one another. We live in a universe that seeks balance. For every action there is an opposite and equal reaction. There is matter and antimatter, electron and proton, attraction and repulsion, good and evil, compassion and indifference.

All our energy centers are made up of opposing energies that should balance one another. In my life, I was always taught to seek and embrace glory, recognition, achievements, joy, creativity, growth and action. However, I can't remember that anyone ever told me the importance of embracing their opposites or any of the other emotions that our society does not celebrate. It took me years and a lot of shame and feeling inadequate to admit that I was ever lonely. I remember sharing this emotion with one of my friends and he was shocked. He said, "Wow! But you are always surrounded by friends. You're so outgoing, so expressive, so full of zest for life. You are the last person that I would ever have thought gets lonely." And yes, all of these observations were true. But behind that truth was a frightened woman obsessed with not being alone and compelled to always have an activity to keep her away from her loneliness. When I was forced to face my loneliness, food became the entertainer, the party, and the distraction that kept me from facing the fear of being alone.

After the 9/11 tragedies, one of the most moving stories I heard was that of Lauren and Greg Manning. Prior to 9/11 Lauren had been physically stunning. She arrived at the elevator doors of World Trade Center Tower 1 just as the jet fuel incinerated the lobby. She suffered severe burns over 82% of her body that left her horribly disfigured. Greg stood by her side and expressed his unwavering love on a daily basis. He loved not just the external beauty but the heart that existed behind that burned and disfigured body. That was real love.

Dilia De La Altagracia

It is so easy to celebrate our achievements and to be proud of ourselves when we look good – to rejoice in our bright ideas, our kind and honorable actions. But the story of Greg and Lauren Manning brings a powerful parallel: True love of self, like true love of another, is achieved only when we can embrace the ugliest aspects of ourselves, our ugliest thoughts and emotions, and not reject but accept and honor that they are part of us.

However, what I kept missing, what I had never really heard any psychologist say, was that it is essential to remain willing to be with *all* of one's feelings. I needed to accept my negative emotions to begin being my best friend, my own best advocate.   This seemed contradictory to me. How could embracing ugly emotions such as anger be good for me? I had to understand that I loving myself just because I was a good person wasn't enough. True self-love meant accepting emotions, perhaps even behaviors, that we have been conditioned to disapprove. I began to realize that I never looked at my son and said, "Today you've been insufferable and I will stop loving you until you change that behavior." My unwillingness to embrace my negative feelings as part of myself was a form of self-rejection. In rejecting my feelings I stopped loving myself and continued to fuel my addiction.

Internally I was conflicted, I kept arguing, "If I accept these negative emotions, won't I start acting them out?" Somehow I confused *being* with my emotions and *acting* out my emotions. It took my desire to be healthy and binge-free, to stop the self-rejection of my FAT body, to accept that the rejection of my "undesirable feelings" was part of what perpetuated my overeating.

I did not want to face my loneliness, my disappointment, or anything that I thought was unpleasant. But I finally surrendered. I had tried all the other alternatives, and the choice was clear: Continue the self-hate of being fat or be with my emotions. I finally realized that to reject any of my emotions was the most profound form of self-hate, because at a primordial level, we are our emotions. It helped me to recognize that all humans feel loneliness, disappointment, anger and boredom, that those are important aspects of the human experience.

I have finally embraced the idea that to live binge-free, to achieve balance in life, I must embrace all my emotions. This means not only the excitement of connection, but also the despair of loneliness; not only the euphoria of achievement, but also the anguish of failure; not only the joy of peace, but also the chaos of anger. All emotions have a dark side. I had made a lifestyle of compulsively pursuing only the "acceptable" version of all my emotions and unconsciously suppressing their "unacceptable" versions.

the sacred no

The time will come when the familiar triggers of overeating will recur. On one of the usual evenings when I was trying to get my son to do his homework, a friend called with an impromptu invitation to catch a movie that I really wanted to see. The kitchen needed cleaning, I'd promised my boss I would complete a task by the next morning, the laundry had piled up, the dog jumped on the counter and broke a treasured piece of china, and the doorbell rang. It was the neighborhood Girl Scouts selling cookies, just what the old habit said I needed. I felt trapped, overwhelmed, frustrated, disappointed, overcommitted, alone, and completely stressed out. Moments like these will happen – count on it, plan for these times. Be ready for them because when they do happen, those Girl Scouts cookies will seem like manna from heaven.

When these situations occur, most of us just throw our hands in the air and say, "to hell with eating well, I have to get through tonight, and those Girl Scouts cookies are my salvation." I had no refusal skills and lacked peace amidst the storm of modern life. The usual rationalizations will surge up in full force: "You know there are only twelve calories per cookie." "I really need a cookie." "It's better to eat the damn cookies than to kick the dog or kill my son." You know what I'm saying. You've been there, done that, bought the T-shirt. This is the reality of most of our lives.

Until I started meditating I had no refuge. I didn't have the ability to pause for that sacred moment when I could be with my feelings or even give them a name – "I feel totally stressed out." "I feel so alone." "I need help." "I need nurturing." "I'm overwhelmed." I couldn't take that split-second pause when options other than the cookies could seriously be considered. Meditation is the only tool I have found to bridge those stressful moments between "to hell with eating well" and finding a nurturing and healing alternative. It gives the emotional elasticity needed to cross the bridge into a healthy set of options instead of having no option but to overeat. For fourteen years I didn't understand the importance of meditation, and every time I chose the cookies I hated myself for not having any willpower. I would eat not just one cookie but the entire box, sometimes a box and a half, or I'd sample all five boxes I had so generously purchased from my neighbor's children.

Dilia De La Altagracia

Until I started meditating, I could not take that moment to breathe deeply and give the Girl Scouts a donation instead of buying the cookies. Even when I told myself I shouldn't, even when I knew better, the same scene played itself out again and again before I learned to meditate: I'd simply gave in and eat in order to cope.

Meditation afforded me that sacred moment to pause and clearly understand that tonight is a school night, I'm a single parent, and I really can't make my boss happy, so I will not take on another commitment. It only takes a quiet moment to decide the laundry doesn't absolutely have to be done this evening. It only takes a moment to decide to be kind to yourself and stop over committing. It is a sacred moment, a healing moment, when you breathe life into your being and begin celebrating who you are. Until I started meditating, that sacred moment didn't exist.

This might be one of the most difficult concepts to convey, but our Western training values overcommitment; it values multitasking and mislabels self-discipline. We don't want to accept the fact that thriving despite the multiple demands of modern society requires the refuge of silence. We have violated our natural rhythms and accelerated our lives beyond their sane capacity. To cope, we must resort to some type of drug, and my drug was food. I finally realized that I must choose to take the time to meditate. The other choice was remaining FAT for the rest of my life. Meditation allowed me the sacred moment to say no to all of these self-destructive behaviors and yes to the vitality of my life.

Starting a meditation program might be as difficult for you as it was for me because it is the antithesis of our modern way of life. But again let me emphasize, meditation was the single most important step I took to stop compulsive overeating. Without it I had no refuge from daily stress. Furthermore, I lacked the wisdom and the skill to pause, to wait, to be aware, so that dysfunctional behavior would not trap me again.

chapter 4: tools for the journey

identify triggering situations:

List situations that consistently trigger overeating behavior in life (add to this list or substitute your own):
- Dealing with a specific person(s) at work – list them all.
- Interacting with family members – list them all.
- Driving during rush hour.
- Being asked to work overtime.
- Being prevented from engaging in an activity because of work or family responsibility. List some examples.
- Feeling overwhelmed with the demands of modern life.
- Boredom – List when you typically experience boredom.
- Anything that causes anxiety.
- Anything that causes disappointment.
- Anything that causes anger.
- List any other emotion that makes you hungry.

exercise:

identify recurring emotions:

1. Aided by my checklist on chapter 3 of the recurring emotions that triggered my emotional hunger, compile your own comprehensive list of whatever leads you to emotional eating.

2. When you have completed your personalized list, go back to each of these situations and visualize, with as much detail as possible, what happens in your body. Begin to breathe into each of these emotional triggers. Record your feelings during the situations that cause you to overeat.

3. Continue breathing to fully bring these emotions to life until you feel that you will be able to sit with them until they dissipate.

4. Record your willingness and ability to breathe into your inner center where the emotional hunger is nourished.

5 - emotions that cause overeating

I had to do several months of yoga before I was able to truly feel some of my emotions. Then I was not able to be with these emotions long enough to let their energy dissipate. Yoga helped me stay with the meditation, and then the meditation helped me sit with my emotions.

It is important to understand that we must readily – as easily as we can zip a pair of pants – be able to identify our emotions. Second, we have to be able to be with those emotions long enough to allow them to dissipate and yield the necessary energy shift that stops us from eating through them. Here is a depiction of how many of us process emotions.

three ways of experiencing emotions

1. blocked feelings, the mind rules, we eat our emotions

The moment there is discomfort, the addiction mechanism triggers the mind to find a solution. Our mind, which functions analytically, blocks our ability to get in touch with the emotion. The discomfort is then presented as emotional hunger. The anticipation of fulfilling the need, now masked as emotional hunger, takes on its own compulsive nature. We begin the search to satisfy our hunger with such zest that everything else seems to be secondary. All of our attention is focused in meeting this "need." We are oblivious to the real and underlying emotion that is fueling the hunger. One reasonable meal or snack doesn't seem to satisfy us because the true need has not been met. The more we eat, the more the hunger seems to intensify. In an effort to satisfy it, we keep eating.

We finally reach the point at which we cannot eat any more. Our stomach is bloated, but even though the triggering emotion has still not been recognized, it is now masked as disgust, shame, disbelief that we have done this again. Being disgusted is a judgment of the mind that perpetuates our inability to get in touch with the underlying emotion.

105

2. we understand it, but the mind is still in charge

The moment we feel emotional discomfort, the addiction mechanism triggers the mind to find a solution. We know it is not hunger but the response mechanism is so engrained that the "hunger" response still comes up. We judge ourselves even more harshly because we "know better." Then we rationale/justify why we should satisfy the hunger. If it is around dinnertime, we justify it by saying that it's time to eat something anyway. However, after several courses, we are still hungry.

Our awareness of the suppressed emotions warns us that we are in bingeing mode. The awareness and knowledge of the mechanism doesn't seem to dispel the hunger; we still want to eat.

We might be able to talk ourselves out of the binge, but something doesn't feel quite right. We are so used to bingeing that that solution keeps creeping back into our minds. We negotiate, we mentally list our options, we try to identify a low-calorie solution, but the only thing we really want to do is binge until we satiate and cannot stomach another bite.

3. the feeling stage: we experience emotions

The mind is tranquil and is not the only resource in charge to generate a solution. We have arrived at a level of maturity in which we experience and honor the wisdom within our bodies. Our emotions flow unobstructed within our bodies. The mind is not blocking emotions with its chatter and a buffet of eating options.

Emotions arise – we recognize them, stop, focus, breathe. We feel the sensations that accompany them. We keep breathing. We follow how the sensations change: Intensity? Dissipate? Move from one part of the body to another? Notice the thoughts that parade through. What are we feeling ourselves is true in this moment? We stay with the process until the emotional wave crests.

We accept all our feelings and do not judge or reject emotions that we were not willing to face in the past because we deemed unacceptable. The emotion is experienced in the body and held in consciousness. There is no judgment, no deadline, no aggression, and no impatience. The emotion is held until it is dissipated, not understood or judged, but dissipated. The chatter of the mind – blame, judgment, or disapproval – is no longer present. Nothing is left to fuel the hunger.

chapter 5: emotions that lead to over-eating

At the beginning of this process, when we start short-circuiting our emotional hunger, we are going to feel as we did when we first received our driver's license. We had to think of everything that needed to be done to drive that car: Which one of these pedals is the brake? How do I signal again? How much do I turn the wheel to go left? How do I parallel park? Where are the windshield wipers? As the weeks pass, and all the knowledge that makes safe driving possible becomes second nature, we drive without giving it a second thought.

When we first embark on this journey, we are going to have to go through the mechanics of how to dissipate the emotional hunger. As with driving, the more we do it the sooner the response will be automatic.

The first step is to feel when emotional hunger kicks in. In some cases all we might know is that we shouldn't be hungry because, for example, we had a huge breakfast just three hours ago, or we're craving very specific foods – a sure sign of nonphysical hunger.

The second step is simply to acknowledge, "I'm emotionally hungry. There must be something within me that's out of balance or that needs to be addressed." Sometimes when I have been writing for three or more hours, the emotional hunger sensation kicks in. I stop writing and simply get up and do something physical for twenty minutes. In other words, I need a break; my body is tired of writing. My mind can continue to push me to write and ignore my other physical needs, but this time I catch it. In the past I used to get a high-calorie candy bar to suppress the real need, now I understand that I need to take a short break. I find during these physical break times that drinking a couple of glasses of water helps tremendously. Ayurvedic healing recommends filling a thermo bottle in the morning with hot water and to complement it with either freshly grated ginger or some type of acidic juice like lemon juice. The idea is to take a few sips every 30 minutes to maintain that sense of well being and balance throughout the day.

The third (and critical) step is to achieve a tranquil mind that allows us to feel the sensations of our bodies. If the issue is not something as simple as taking a break, breathe into the emotion with healing intentions. Slowly and deliberately send nourishing oxygen into all parts of your body. Recognize fully whatever arises, offering no resistance or desire to fix it or escape from it. Be totally present in the moment and feel whatever emotion is masking itself as hunger. If need be, keep a list of the top emotions that caused you to overeat in the past. I had to ask myself: Am I feeling anxious? Disappointed? Sad? Overwhelmed? You get the idea. Write down your own list of the emotions that cause overeating for you, so you can refer to it if you are having difficulty identifying the emotion.

Once you find the feeling, the fourth step is to keep breathing deeply until you are in the present moment with it. There is no past or future; there is only you and your feeling.

The fifth step is to be your own best friend who can provide the inner dialogue of nurture and support as you go past the anxiety and the resistance. Suppressed feelings will keep manifesting as emotional hunger. By simply staying in the moment with the feelings – being truly present without judgment, agenda or blame – and allowing those feelings to be experienced for as long as necessary, the emotional hunger will disappear. Sometimes there is much tension and struggle in this fifth step, and we must then meditate or assume a yoga posture until we can feel the energy shift.

Don't confuse being with your feelings with expressing them or acting them out. This is not about calling your best friend to say, "I'm feeling lonely," or "I'm so mad," or hurling dishes against the wall. This is about allowing feelings to enter our consciousness with acceptance and being with them until they stop masking themselves as emotional hunger.

emotions that lead to overeating

In my journey I discovered that 80% of my overeating was caused by just a few emotions. In the interest of demonstrating what it takes to be with these emotions, how easy it is to misinterpret them, and what pitfalls to avoid, I'm including my overeating trigger emotions and how I sit with them.

boredom

One emotion that leads to overeating is boredom. And how do we escape from boredom? We snack. Americans have raised snacking to an art form.

chapter 5: emotions that lead to over-eating

As I analyzed boredom, I began to see a pattern. I had scheduled myself to do something I really didn't want to do, but I had to do it because I was up against a deadline. There was always something else interesting or entertaining for me to do instead of the task that I was avoiding, but sooner or later I would have to stay home and do laundry, pay the bills, clean the house, or something else that I really didn't enjoy. I made a list of activities to help shift my energy:

- Write down the benefits of getting the task done.
- Take a rewarding 15 or 20 minute break every time you finish one of the boring tasks. For me the reward was reading a chapter of a book that I thoroughly enjoyed or doing a search on an interesting topic on the Web.
- Chew gum, something appealing – spicy cinnamon is my favorite.
- Put on some high energy music while doing the boring task.
- Do 10 minutes of fast paced exercise.
- Last option: chew on something healthy but low in calories.

Now, as I revisit the list, I can see that in the end, despite my best intentions, I would resort to eating to combat the boredom. When I meditated to gauge why I was feeling bored, I discovered that boredom was a facade I was using to avoid facing disappointment, shame, anxiety, depression or frustration. My unwillingness to be bored was, again, a form of self-rejection: a denial of buried emotions

As with all suppressed emotions, sooner or later we will eat through boredom in an effort to feel better. For me, the solution is not to ask, "Why am I bored?" but, "What am I trying to avoid?" Then the challenge of overcoming the boredom becomes not so much a matter of formulating an activity but of being with the underlying emotion until it is thoroughly processed and dissipated. Only then will the hunger go away.

The lesson in the story is that when you are bored and want to eat, meditate. Uncover what the boredom is hiding and process that emotion. Keep asking yourself, "From which emotion am I trying to hide? From which emotion am I trying to escape?"

stress

For many people stress is the leading cause of overeating. When I started my research about stress, I found numerous books, websites and lists on coping with stress. The advice most of them gave was:

- Be more organized.
- Anticipate anything that could go wrong and work around it to alleviate the discomfort.
- Change your mind about the thing that causes you stress.
- Do something nice for yourself.
- Seek the support of others.

In the end, the messages were loud and clear: you can reduce stress by avoiding it, ignoring it or minimizing your exposure to it. I find nothing life enhancing or realistic about a strategy that is predicated on avoidance. The reality is that most of us already know dozens of ways to cope with stress, and yet somehow we never get around to making that second set of car keys. The fact that we do know how to manage the stress in our lives – at least intellectually – makes us feel even more inadequate because we think we should be better organized.

Stress is a subjective mental reaction to the external events in our world. One person may become angry or tense during rush hour traffic and arrive at the office stressed. A different person accepts that there is absolutely nothing he can do about how badly traffic is backed up and chooses to pass the time listening to music. This person shows up for work relaxed and energized. Same conditions, different interpretations, different experiences; one leads to stress, one does not.

Like boredom, stress is a symptom of underlying imbalance. Perhaps the person who arrives at work anxious from the morning rush hour has suppressed control or anger issues. In that case, she might consider undertaking some self-discovery to find the source that fuels the stress. I discovered that in most cases stress is a symptom of unexplored anger, irritability, anxiety, hopelessness, or depression. Disappointment in myself, disappointment in others, inability to say no (which led to overcommitment), control issues, or any combination of these emotions all manifested themselves as stress.

The person who arrives at the office relaxed and energized has surrendered any need to control the situation and has made a conscious

chapter 5: emotions that lead to over-eating

decision to observe rush-hour traffic almost the way one would watch a movie. He chooses not to get emotionally involved in the trauma. This level of conscious choice can then be taken one step further by not befriending those addicted to trauma or drama and by not trying to interpret other people's actions. Stress caused by lack of control over the external environment causes one to behave like an emotional ATM: Someone pushes button x, I automatically spit out emotion y.

Many of us experience catharsis when we recognize how our negative interpretation of events creates our emotional reality. Situations such as driving to work made me confront my interpretation of what I chose to make rush hour traffic mean. By extension, I had an emotional release when I understood the futility of trying to exert control over an uncontrollable situation. This led to a different set of choices: I could get up earlier or later in order to go to work before or after rush hour. That was an informed choice arising from self-love, not denial. If I chose to drive in rush hour, then I accepted being in rush hour, embraced my lack of control, and accepted the futility of getting stressed. I found that I could take advantage of the extra time before getting to work by enjoying some good music, catching up on the news, or listening to an insightful audio book.

We also need to be selective about our relaxation time. Mass media bombards us with messages about what we should buy, how we should look, what we have to do to measure up – and those are just the commercials. Add to that the images of brutality and inhumanity from the newscasts and from all the violent programs, and it becomes clear that there is nothing relaxing about this form of entertainment. Yet I remember when I took no responsibility for its effect on my life.

We must, however, perceive emotional hunger in a larger context. We are not wired to be plugged in every waking minute of the day, to live at the frantic pace at which we force ourselves to function, nor with the number of commitments and activities that many of us have been brainwashed to undertake. I remember the days when my definition of relaxation was to watch a couple hours of TV, yet I convinced myself that I didn't have time to meditate. It is ironic that the level of stress I accepted fueled so much of my overeating. Finally motivated by self-love, I experienced the benefits of meditating for twenty minutes and watching only an hour and forty minutes of selective entertainment.

I now understand and love myself enough to realize that stress leads me to overeat, and accepting that connection is in my best interest. I love myself enough to say no to additional commitments. I love myself enough to bring true relaxation into my life. I love myself enough to meditate so that stress does not fuel overeating as a coping mechanism. I'm willing to be with whatever emotion lies underneath the stress and hold it in loving consciousness until it dissipates.

loneliness

For the longest time I thought that the antidote for loneliness was to collect enough friends so that one of them would be there when I felt the old emptiness. After a very introverted time in high school and college, I blossomed and became outgoing. When I was around others, I was interesting, expressive, lively, and exciting. I believed that all I had to do to escape loneliness was to reach for meaningful connections or remind myself that many people loved me and that I could call on them when I was lonely. I kept repeating the message that loneliness is a normal part of modern life, and I did not need to blame myself for that.

By eating to mitigate loneliness, I was trading one difficult emotion for another. After overeating I could focus on the self-hate caused by overeating and effectively ignore the pangs of loneliness. I needed to understand that overeating was not making me feel loved, that it only postponed my sense of loneliness.

I read a lot of advice about how to deal with loneliness instead of eating. Some of the literature does make sense. Loneliness is definitely the profound separation we feel in this society, many times while in the midst of a crowd. Calling a friend instead of blindly bingeing does help. Building deep and significant relationships is important not only for losing weight; it is one of the cornerstones of a full and meaningful life.

I also know, however, that for people who are overwhelmingly shy the concept that all they have to do is form more meaningful friendships is a cruel insult. André Dubus once stated, "Shyness has a strange element of narcissism, a belief that how we look, how we perform, is truly important to other people." If this is your issue, sit with this quote and journal on its meaning.

Shyness was not my issue. I had plenty of friends. I could write gut wrenching emails and demand to be heard. But at the end of the day I had to be with my loneliness. I had to come to an empty house, and my

chapter 5: emotions that lead to over-eating

inclination was not to call a friend. The idea of just phoning and saying I was lonely somehow did not seem practical to me. What was I going to do? Call every night and say I'm lonely again? I had to ask myself if my friendships were superficial. Granted, I did have the feeling of not being understood. I knew I was someone who thought too much and did not have the ability to share certain insights with some of my friends. They were friends for whom certain topics, religion or politics for example, were just a means of getting into a maze of disagreement, and I saw no point in that. There were other friends who had the biggest hearts but with whom I found no intellectual stimulation.

I gained the most healing insight when I looked at my side of the friendship equation. Was I worthy of love? Was I was worthy of friendship? The answer to these questions was a barely audible no. I know I have friends and family who truly love me, but my deep feeling of inadequacy was getting in the way. I had difficulty letting love in and feeling good enough to be worthy of love. My biggest fear in life is that I am not worthy of being loved. I had been brainwashed into believing that I needed to look like the latest magazine cover model or have specific emotional collateral to bargain with so I could be worth loving. I just didn't feel that I was worth loving because of who I am, regardless of what I did for others or what I looked like. Until that lack of adequacy was healed, no one in the world could make me feel loved. That was the origin of my abysmal sense of loneliness. It had nothing to do with being popular or having deep connections. Rather, it was a loneliness I had to heal within myself, with the transformational power of self-love.

You, as an emotional eater, must realize that if you continue living as a human doing instead of a human being – if, for example, you run to the phone every time you feel lonely – you will not be able to change your overeating behavior for the long term. Friends will grow weary of once again having to hear about your issues, of never being able to really share with you the issues that might be bothering them. Eventually, they might see your number on the caller ID and decide that they don't have the time or emotional energy to deal with you, or they might become brutally honest and tell you that you need to address the source of your loneliness.

To achieve healing it is critical to sit with the loneliness. Once I did that, I began to feel its source; I began to see loneliness in its ultimate form of self-rejection. Within the feeling of loneliness is a sense that something necessary for our happiness is missing. I had built an exterior life of meaningless activity from which I returned home and ate to fill the emotional void.

I convinced myself that I needed to form a bond with a man, that the issue of my loneliness existed because I did not share my life with a partner. To satisfy this belief, I pursued relationships, but always with a list of insatiable needs that I expected a man to fulfill (I saw them as "qualities" I was looking for in a man).

The list became very specific. My euphoria was tangible when someone came close to matching the qualities in THE LIST. Of course my concept of the ideal man prevented any possibility that I might learn to love him for who he really was.

These relationships seemed to work while there was an equitable fulfillment of needs. For most men, the need was for sex. For me it was the need to feel that which I could not generate within myself. As those relationships settled into the reality of life, and my new lover did not satisfy my unfulfilled needs, the list of qualities became a list of grievances which turned into edible disappointments. Sooner instead of later, the relationships went down the drain and I went back to eating my loneliness. Now I realize that any healthy man would never take on the burden for the happiness I could not find within myself.

I continued to sit with the loneliness. But this time I was willing to stay with it until it became the fear of being alone and the disappointment that I was not good enough. I began to feel the fear and disappointment in my heart, and because I was not trying to escape, I stopped searching for relationships to end the loneliness. I began to ask what it would take for me to be good enough. Through the healing power of self-love, all these feelings of loneliness stopped, and at last I no longer have the driving emptiness that I want to fill with food.

disappointment

Even as I was going through the process of learning how to be with my emotions, I fooled myself into alternatives in order to avoid the pain.

I was out with friends one Friday night when I unexpectedly met a man and spent the last hours of the evening with him. There was definitely an attraction, and he walked me to my car and kissed me goodnight. Before things got heated, I suggested that we should "do the dinner thing" and told him to call in the after noon the next day. Noon came and went. My son, who was at his dad's house, called and said that he wanted to come to my house. I told him I was going out, so he needed to stay with his dad as planned. My son explained that he didn't mind being in my house by himself. He was at an age when he didn't understand that going out on a date meant that I might want some privacy. I felt rather guilty, and I lacked the courage to explain the situation.

Prior to the Friday night connection, I had made plans to meet a girlfriend for dinner and catch some live music. I called her in the morning to cancel our plans and to share my joy at meeting someone the night before. As most single women would be, my friend was elated for me and fully supported canceling our plans so I could have dinner with my newfound interest.

Afternoon arrived, and I fussed over what to wear, where to suggest we eat, questions I wanted to ask, how I should do my hair – the usual pre-date jitters. Early afternoon turned into late afternoon, and I finally realized that he was not going to call. I phoned my girlfriend back to ask if she had made other plans. She was so gracious, still available and we had a pleasant dinner. I shared the events, but I also told her how proud I was that I didn't sit home waiting for this guy to call. After dinner we went on to enjoy some live music and have a couple of drinks. Overall, it was a very pleasant evening and, more importantly, I believed I had dealt with my feelings and that was that. But when I came home, despite a lovely and very satisfying dinner, and having absolutely no reason to be hungry, I began to eat.

I finally saw that my pride was serving as a mask to hide disappointment. I realized that I needed to face my disappointment or I would eat through it. As a statement of how I felt, I told myself, "I was really disappointed that you didn't call today. I had to fumble plans, put off my son, put my friend on standby, and resist coming home because I didn't want to spend Saturday night by myself. It felt good when I finally told myself, "He hasn't called so, what the hell, I'll go have dinner with a friend. I refuse to put my life on hold for you. I need to move on."

Only when I started feeling clearly, "I'm disappointed. I'm really, really disappointed," and I sat down to be with the disappointment did the hunger go away. I believed that by verbalizing the facts to my friend and by going out that I was not feeling sorry for myself. It never occurred to me that I didn't allow myself to experience the disappointment. So in the end, even after having a great dinner with a friend, even after enjoying an evening of live music, I came home hungry; I was still trying to eat the disappointment I had not fully felt and exhausted.

The wonderful thing about being willing to sit with my emotions was that I got to the root of my feelings. Yes, I was disappointed and thought all I had to do was find an alternative to deal with the disappointment. I even felt proud of myself for moving on. But, as always, whenever I don't allow myself to fully feel the emotion, sooner or later, even after having been satisfied physically with food, I'm still hungry. The avoided emotion was still lurking unprocessed in the background. Going out seemed like a good idea, and it probably was, but I needed to sit with the emotion first. Yes, I had expressed my feelings to my friend, but it was an intellectual exercise, the bravado of "I'm not going to take that crap from anyone." It was talking about the feelings rather than experiencing them. All these alternatives are forms of avoidance, and in the end, they never stop the emotional hunger.

anxiety

Anxiety is one of the major components of overeating. Sometimes we call it compulsiveness. Anxiety is the violation of our natural human rhythm, the unwillingness to slow down, make allowance for quiet time, celebrate spending three hours with our children, fixing something that needs to be fixed, or just doing nothing.

Underlying much of my anxiety was the fear that I was not good enough, attractive enough, or smart enough. Those fears motivated me to take on more than any human being should take on. For most of my life, I have been classified a super-achiever. I prided myself on this and always took on more than the lion's share of whatever activity I participated in. I am a single mother and sole breadwinner. I receive financial support from no one. I have a son, a house, cars, pets, friends, a social life, and interests. I have difficulty saying "No", even when I'm asked to do something unreasonable. More importantly, I have a history of failing to take care of myself. My needs were never a priority, so I could never treat them as scheduled events in my life; I could always set them aside to take care of someone else.

I need to exercise, to feel that my life is in order, to have fun, to have the basics of life addressed. I have the emotional need to grow, and to feel the beauty of life. I have a spiritual need to feel connected to something beyond this human experience, something that for me is manifested in the amazement of nature, the beauty of art, the laughter

chapter 5: emotions that lead to over-eating

of children, the kindness of others. Because I lived with the underlying fear that I was not good enough, I never understood that it was healthy to schedule time for myself to take care of these needs. I learned that I had to consider my time sacred. Then I could schedule other priorities such as the needs of my son, my family, my friends, and my work. Typically the scheduling priorities were:

1. Work
2. My son
3. Responsibilities related to the infrastructure of my life: car, house, bills, insurance renewal, parent-teacher conferences and the rest.
4. Friends

For most of my life, I was never a priority; work always came first. Of course, work provides the means to support life, but it is interesting that many of us have turned the equation around and made work the driving force in our lives. Even though it is supposed to support life, it becomes the factor that defines our lives. I remember when all my friends came from my work environment and all my social activities were with people from work. As I moved into new job situations, I lost touch with the people from the old job and made new friends in the new office.

To lower our anxiety, we must take the initial step of clarifying our priorities. If we don't define ourselves as the first priority of our lives, we have to examine how we have defined quality of life. How are our choices affected when we have a low supply of energy, joy, vitality, peace of mind and wisdom? Choices to meditate, exercise, go to yoga class and select foods based on the need for vitality are driven by self-love. Having these nurturing activities as priorities lowers our anxiety level, and the fuel that drives overeating is depleted.

The fascinating development is that taking care of myself has not created an egotistical monster. Instead I have more time for my son now, and I consciously attend to his needs. I am present for my friends and find more joy in spending time with them. They have commented on how much nicer it is to be with a less driven and high-strung person. I make more careful choices about how to spend my time. I have, for example, cut back TV time to almost nothing. In following my inner guidance, which is self-love expressed, the overall quality of my life has improved a hundredfold.

control

Another issue that caused anxiety was my desire to gain control over my environment. I became more anxious when I lost control, and the more I needed to calm down the hungrier I became. The more I sat with the need to have control, the more I realized I had convinced myself I needed to control events or other's behaviors. I had constructed a world with specific rules and guidelines, and when people didn't measure up to expectations, my anxiety level went up. Do you know how stressed most people become after being in traffic for 30 minutes more than they had calculated? Do you know how most of us deal with that kind of anxiety?

I discovered that I could either accept the traffic or continue my frantic need to be right about how long the commute should take, when I was supposed to arrive at work, and when life was supposed to happen. The choice was entirely mine. I chose to let go of the notion of control because, frankly, my options were either to be in control and eat through the lack of it or to accept that I don't have control over anyone or anything.

Once I got past the anxiety and sat with the fear underlying it, I dealt with the most horrible scenarios that I had concocted in my head such as getting fired, losing my house, or never finding a mate and living the rest of my life alone. I faced fully the pain of these self-created horrors. Then, paradoxically, I felt a tremendous sense of peace. It wasn't until I sat with the fears that existed entirely in my head that I clearly saw the high cost of control in my life. I was driven and motivated by my illusion of control, and the only way I knew to cope with it was by eating.

It is difficult and time consuming to find new work, but I have finally discovered that I no longer fear losing my job. I'm a hard-working, effective, dedicated and committed employee. I have had to come to terms with the difference between selling forty hours of my time and selling the quality of my life. Any job that necessitates giving up the quality of life is not in my best interest. It is not a job that will support my decision to live without an eating addiction.

By facing my fears, I am no longer driven by what friends might think or whether they won't like me if I place myself as my first priority. I am also no longer driven by the fear of not finding someone to share my life. The reality is that I have had partner choices, but none of the choices has been so compelling that I chose to give up my single life. After being with the loneliness, I have finally decided that while I would like to share my life with a loving partner, it is better to live alone than to live in conflict. More importantly, I realize that any relationship forged by the fear of not having a partner is not likely to be worthwhile and joyous.

By facing the fear that masked itself as the need to control, I've almost eliminated anxiety. Ninety-eight percent of my life is now anxiety-free, and on the rare occasion when anxiety does occur, I don't have to eat through it.

anger

"Everything that irritates us about others can lead us to an understanding about ourselves."

- Carl Jung

We must identify whether anger is one of our triggering emotions. Many of us stuff down our anger with food. In corporate America the message is loud and clear: it is not OK for a woman – or a man for that matter – to express anger in any form. Such behavior unsettles office decorum. Women often give in to the demands of others in order to avoid conflict. Those compromises frequently lead to resentment and finally to overeating. There are more than 1,000 books on the subject of anger; most of them advise us on how to "express" anger in a suitable and appropriate manner. Others address the management of anger. Whenever I felt angry, I only knew that I needed to calm down if I wanted to keep my job, and food was the ultimate tranquilizer. The social reality of our lives requires behavior that is appropriate to the occasion. For me, the more important task was finding the source of my anger, especially when it was recurrent and persistent. By merely learning how to express our emotions in an acceptable manner, how to "manage our anger," aren't we ultimately suppressing it?

While some anger is a normal life experience, the question for us must be, "Is anger a primary emotion that drives me to overeat?" If we tend to get angry more often than the average person, and anger is a chronic emotion in our lives, then it is in our best interest to understand and heal the root causes of it.

Dilia De La Altagracia

I have a friend, Wyatt, whose mother left when he was three years old. His dad did his best to raise Wyatt and his sister, but there has always been a profound anger in my friend's life. This anger seems to lead him into confrontations and conflicts in all aspects of his life. At work he gets into more fights than all the rest of his co-workers combined. Moreover, Wyatt has quit many jobs out of sheer frustration only to create similar conflicts in the next work environment. Relaxing in a bar with Wyatt is not really relaxing. We always have to watch him when he drinks too much because sooner or later he will find someone with whom to fight. Wyatt lives wounded by childhood abandonment and somehow has to demonstrate through anger that he doesn't need anyone.

The most profound insight is to discover the fuel that feeds the fire. It is not healthy or normal to live in constant conflict with anger as a driving force in life. Anyone who exhibits that type of behavior must understand its source and be aware of wounds leading to an automatic emotional trigger that can only be suppressed with food or other addictions.

There are thousands of qualified psychotherapists who could help many of us identify and name the source of our anger. But understanding its source is only the first step. As with all emotions, sitting with and breathing into the anger and continuing to do bodywork are effective mitigations. The longer I sat with the anger, the clearer it became that the issue was not as I perceived. The fuel that fed the anger was my helplessness in dealing with specific persons or situations.

Paradoxically, expressing anger is actually a way of suppressing the underlying feeling. The Quaker idea of witnessing ourselves is a much more effective approach. Once I was willing to face and name my helplessness, I was able to dissipate the anger. But because it was recurring and persistent, and I wanted to stop overeating, I began to look at how to heal the sense of helplessness. I once again turned to bodywork, specifically yoga, and began to work on the power center, the third chakra, where the emotion of helplessness is concentrated. By working with yoga postures and holding them with healing intent, I began to get clarity about what caused my sense of helplessness, and I was able to stop confusing it with anger.

chapter 5: emotions that lead to over-eating

the blues

Getting the blues, the state in which we are not clinically depressed but nothing seems interesting, does lead many of us to overeat. Once again, the feeling triggers the discomfort, and the mind compensates by projecting emotional hunger.

Whenever I sat with the feelings that masked themselves as the blues, I found a mixture of boredom, disappointment and sadness. There was never a pure and clear feeling that I could call the blues. So, like boredom and sadness, I had to confront it. I found it helpful to ask questions such as: "Am I bored, disappointed, or sad?" If it was disappointment or sadness, I would keep breathing with healing intentions and ask, "What am I sad about?" If it was boredom, I asked, "What is the boredom masking?" I sat with these emotions until they manifested themselves fully and completely and I was able to feel them unequivocally. That is the only way to remove the fuel that drives emotional hunger.

fatigue

Being overweight takes away most of the vitality of life, and feeling tired becomes a perpetual state. Being overweight causes fatigue in three ways: First is the physical strain of carrying around a heavy overcoat of fat. If you are thirty-five pounds overweight, it is like carrying a five-gallon pail of water all the time, even taking it to bed with you. Forty pounds of extra weight is like carrying a bowling ball in each hand. Fifty pounds overweight is like carrying two twenty-five pound bags of sugar with you wherever you go. Sixty pounds overweight is like carrying a bale of hay.

The second cause of fatigue is the emotional weight of not being socially acceptable or sexually desirable. The third is that many times we do not get a good night's sleep. The anxiety and pace of modern life make it difficult for us to turn off our minds. We try reading, vacuuming, late-night TV or a snack, and finally exhaust our bodies into sleep. When we're awakened by the alarm clock the next morning and have to push our bodies into work, the only way to get through the day is by overeating. While being tired is not an emotion, but a state of being, it is one of the top nine reasons I overate.

Somehow, when I was tired, I did not have the emotional follow-through to sustain my personal desire to be healthy and to remind myself of my goals and my desire to live from a sense of my vitality. The first thing I craved was coffee with lots of cream. I needed it not only to stay awake but also to do a job that I was not physically awake to perform. Our minds can bully us into pushing ourselves beyond the boundaries of well being. The only way to deal with being tired without overeating is meditation. When we are tired, our ability to reason is compromised. We must either sleep, exercise to get a short energy burst, or meditate. We are too tired to invoke reason; we are too tired even to say no to food.

If you are chronically tired, the most important step is to remove the causes. You have to start caring for yourself enough to say no to the recurrent conditions that cause perpetual tiredness.

As with most other states of being, it is important to honor yourself and simply say, "I'm tired." Accept your fatigue and yield to the wisdom of the body.

Fatigue is one of the most difficult states in which to avoid overeating. When we are tired, we want one thing and one thing only – respite. In situations where neither sleep nor exercise are possible, we need to pre-define a strategy for how to deal with tiredness without overeating. Remember, once you become tired, it will be too late to avoid overeating. It is critical to formulate a plan to access effective options before being tired takes over.

tired at home

If it is around bedtime, go to sleep. You might laugh and say, "Duh, of course you should go to sleep." But if we are tired when we get home, most of us need to first fulfill the sense of belonging, of being welcomed, of feeling a sense of home. This need, when not addressed, will manifest itself as cooking something and being comforted with food.

As simple as this sounds, most of us who cope with food compulsions – because we have overeaten in the past when we were tired – will want to eat something. The psychologists with whom I discussed this explained that when we are tired we want to be comforted. Non-emotional eaters also need this sense of belonging, but they fulfill it with a hot bath, or some soothing music, or they snuggle up with a good book or keep movies at home that generate a sense of beauty, serenity and security.

I now know that when I get home, I need to be comforted. I walk around and reacquaint myself with my home, play some soothing music, do an evening yoga tape, write an email to a friend, or read a relaxing book while I sit by the fireplace.

You know what truly comforts you. Make a list – not of what other people find comforting, not what comforts people in the movies, but what you find comforting about being at home. Memorize that list, but also tape it to the refrigerator or your bathroom mirror. Make a deal with yourself that you will know where to find your list so that when you feel tired, and your first reaction is to overeat, you will have alternatives readily available. It is critical to be ready to break the cycle by telling yourself, "Eating is only going to make me feel better for a few minutes. Then I'm going to feel bad about myself. I'm sick of being overweight, and I refuse to give into the old pattern. I'm tired. What would make me feel soothed?"

So the challenge when you arrive home tired is:

1. To fulfill the nesting need
2. To fulfill the need for comfort
3. To fulfill the need for safety and a sense of belonging
4. To fulfill the need to feel unanimously and thoroughly at home, free to do whatever you wish
5. To disrupt the deeply embedded pattern of eating when you are not physically hungry

It is critical to understand that even when the first four steps are accomplished, we still want to eat. The pattern of overeating is that deeply rooted. We cannot be unconscious or flippant about this reality. We must use every means available to override the behavior.

tired at work

Choose tasks that are engaging. If possible, avoid repetitive or boring tasks. Sometimes when you are tired at work, you don't want to tackle tasks that require some brain stimulation or creativity. If you must work on boring and repetitive tasks, play high-energy music.

The implication of this strategy is that you must have the means to play the music at work – a CD or MP3 player or your computer. You must compile a list of music that you find stimulating, and you must have that CD or playlist available at work when you get tired.

If you must have coffee, have condiments available that are consistent with your eating plan. Again, you need to make all these arrangements when you are not tired; because once you are tired, if these choices are not readily available, you will certainly overeat.

Meditation is one of the most effective tools to deal with being tired without overeating. It takes time to develop, but with practice you will be able to use this tool whenever you become tired. The choice to master meditation will be motivated by a desire to have powerful options available instead of overeating.

why can't I sleep?

If your sleeping patterns are erratic, and it is difficult for you to get a good night's sleep, read about sleeping hygiene. This includes following a fixed bedtime and waking time. Make the bedroom quiet, cozy, clean and neat, free of anything that is not conducive to sleep. Block the incoming light if sunlight wakes you up; get rid of excessive houseplants. At night, plants absorb oxygen and give off carbon dioxide. In essence, by having a massive number of plants in your bedroom you are competing for oxygen and inhaling a substance toxic to humans. You might even want to invest in a sound system that cycles through one relaxing CD all night long (I have one of these, and it's wonderful). Don't drink anything – even water – two to three hours before going to sleep. Don't eat foods at dinnertime that cause heartburn in the middle of the night. A stuffed stomach and alcohol helps us getting to sleep initially, but as soon as the blood sugar level drops, anywhere from 2 to 4 hours after going to sleep, you will be wide awake, perhaps with a headache, and you won't be able to sleep for 1 to 2 hours.

chapter 5: emotions that lead to over-eating

After enjoying wine for many years I finally stopped drinking late at night because I realized the negative effect it has on my sleeping pattern. Other things that contribute to poor sleeping:

- Lack of exercise contributes to poor sleeping habits.
- If you can't sleep because of a high-stress life that makes it difficult for you to quiet your mind, you have yet another compelling reason to meditate.
- A very full stomach also contributes to erratic sleeping patterns.

exercise:

For a week do not change anything in your behavior, simply chart the following:

- Track the time that you ate.
- Categorize it as physical or emotional eating
- Rate your anxiety level: calm and serene, normal, stressed, FRAZZLED
- If the eating was labeled "Emotional" can you name the emotions you were feeling before you ate?

Emotional Eating				
	7-9 AM	9-11 AM	11-1 PM	1-3 PM
Day 1 Physical/emotional Anxiety level Name the emotion				
Day 2 Physical/emotional Anxiety level Name the emotion				
Day 3 Physical/emotional Anxiety level Name the emotion				
Day 4 Physical/emotional Anxiety level Name the emotion				
Day 5 Physical/emotional Anxiety level Name the emotion				
Day 6 Physical/emotional Anxiety level Name the emotion				
Day 7 Physical/emotional Anxiety level Name the emotion				

7 Day Eating Plan				
	3-5 PM	5-7 PM	7-9 PM	> 9 PM
Day 1 Physical/emotional Anxiety level Name the emotion				
Day 2 Physical/emotional Anxiety level Name the emotion				
Day 3 Physical/emotional Anxiety level Name the emotion				
Day 4 Physical/emotional Anxiety level Name the emotion				
Day 5 Physical/emotional Anxiety level Name the emotion				
Day 6 Physical/emotional Anxiety level Name the emotion				
Day 7 Physical/emotional Anxiety level Name the emotion				

6 - **the program**

assess your life skills

The following is an assessment of your readiness to embark on this program. It is critical that you answer the questions as honestly as possible. This is not a popularity test. It is not an evaluation of how good a person you are. It is a minimal assessment of whether or not it makes sense for you to embark on a program that requires a tremendous amount of introspection and courage.

We are all human. Our humanity means that we have emotional needs, that we are encouraged or discouraged by the people and events in our lives. If our emotional needs are not being met, it is only natural that our self-esteem is affected. If the life skills that allow us to undertake a transformational program are not present, we are setting ourselves up for failure, which will only lead to lower self-esteem and once again over-eating.

It would make more sense to work on bolstering the necessary life skills before embarking on The End of Diets program. In fact, most psychologists believe that without these skills we cannot achieve long-term progress toward emotional growth. Please be completely honest with yourself when answering the following questions. Consider it an inventory of your needs:

Yes	No	
❑	❑	Do you live with a supportive person or persons?
❑	❑	Is your family life fulfilling?
❑	❑	Do you have family/friends that are emotionally supportive?
❑	❑	Do you feel confident that you can form meaningful relationships?
❑	❑	Do you find your career worthwhile? If you are a stay at home parent, do you find your parenting worthwhile? If you are retired, are your days filled with satisfying activities?

Yes	No	
❏	❏	Do you like your work, coworkers, and boss? If you are a stay at home parent or retired, do you like your immediate circle of friends?
❏	❏	Do you have meaningful problem solving skills?
❏	❏	Do you feel you have skills or talents that others appreciate?
❏	❏	Do you generate a satisfactory income using your talents? If you are a stay at home parent or if you are retired, are you confident about your finances?
❏	❏	Are you happy most of the time?
❏	❏	Do you know how to have a good time?
❏	❏	Do you have hobbies that you pursue on a weekly basis, that you want to master and that are a source of pleasure?
❏	❏	Do you believe that you are a worthwhile person?
❏	❏	Do people like you?
❏	❏	Do you think your life is meaningful?
❏	❏	Do you feel that you add positively to the lives of friends and family members?
❏	❏	Do you have a purpose in life?
❏	❏	Do you consider yourself part of one or more communities?
❏	❏	Do you devote any of your work, effort, or thought to people who are not in your family or immediate circle of friends?
❏	❏	Do you believe that most people are good and that the world is a safe place?
❏	❏	Do you know if you've experienced any childhood issues that need resolution?
❏	❏	Are there past traumatic experiences that cause recurring negative or debilitating feelings in your life? (For example: traumatic assault, sexual abuse, toxic or abusive parents, etc.)
❏	❏	Do you accept yourself even though you are overweight?
❏	❏	Do you have the ability to set healthy boundaries for yourself?
❏	❏	Do you have the ability to say no to others when their requests negatively impact your personal priorities?

chapter 6 – the program

Yes	No	
❑	❑	Do you ask for help when you need assistance with problems and difficulties?
❑	❑	Do you think you are worthy of love as you are right now? (As opposed to: Does something have to improve in your life before you are worthy of love? Will you be worthy of love when you lose weight?)
❑	❑	Do you know what your priorities are in life?
❑	❑	Are you your best friend? Do you possess the self-love to be your own best friend?
❑	❑	Do you feel that others take your needs and wants into consideration when they are prioritizing their plans?
❑	❑	Do you feel that you take good care of yourself? (For example: Do you eat well, exercise consistently, have regular dental or medical checkups?)
❑	❑	Do you celebrate your accomplishments, large or small? (For example do you have an internal dialogue that goes something like this: "I did so great," "I said just the right thing," "I came up with just the right idea." Do you celebrate little achievements throughout the day?)
❑	❑	Do you feel that you have friends, family or mentors who help you develop your full potential?
❑	❑	Do you invest time and/or training to develop your creative ideas?
❑	❑	Do you go out at least once a week just to have fun?
❑	❑	Are you able to talk to yourself with compassion and forgiveness?
❑	❑	Are your office, house and/or car a reflection of what you consider beautiful?
❑	❑	Do you feel that you have friends, family or mentors who support and celebrate with you when you need it?
❑	❑	Do you reward yourself in ways that do not involve food?
❑	❑	Do know how to provide yourself nurturing and constructive criticism?
❑	❑	Do you have confidence in your abilities?
❑	❑	Do you love your body?
❑	❑	Do you see the good qualities of your body?
❑	❑	Do you give yourself what you need and feel good about indulging yourself?

Yes	No	
❑	❑	Do you believe you have an nurturing inner parent when you embark on a large and difficult endeavor such as changing eating behavior?
❑	❑	Do you feel that you are in touch with your emotions?
❑	❑	Do you feel that you know which emotions or situations cause you to overeat?
❑	❑	Do you embrace and then pursue your ideas?
❑	❑	Do you have enjoyable activities, such as happy hours with friends, going to live performance, etc. scheduled during your free time?
❑	❑	Do you trust your intuition?
❑	❑	Do you make balanced and responsible rules for yourself?
❑	❑	Do you take credit for your accomplishments?
❑	❑	Do you trust yourself implicitly?
❑	❑	Do you nourish yourself with good food and good ideas?
❑	❑	Do you avoid comparing yourself to magazine models or TV and movie actors or actresses?
❑	❑	Do you give others authority over your time, resources, or plans?
❑	❑	Do you feel that you have a strong and approving "inner" parent?
❑	❑	Do you feel you have the ability to manage your negative thoughts?
❑	❑	Do you have the ability to turn any recurring negative thoughts into positive affirmations?

do you possess the necessary life skills?

The questions in the above assessment are an attempt to identify how your personal assets compare with the list of specific life skills that follows. These skills are typically found in persons who overcome addictive behavior, in fact they are seen as necessary to overcoming such behavior. This list was formulated by Dr. Peter Monti in his manual for alcoholism counselors titled *Treating Alcohol Dependence.*

Problem-Solving Skills – An important life skill possessed by people who are able to overcome addictive behavior is problem solving. A person with good problem-solving skills, when faced with a difficult

chapter 6 – the program

issue in life, will face the problem head on, formulate options, consider the pros and cons of each option and work on the problem until it is solved. In contrast, the addictive personality dwells on the distress felt when challenging life situations are encountered, feels justified, and takes these feelings as carte blanche for avoiding responsibility, consequently becoming more likely to seek solace in food. Please note that having problem solving skills does not entail avoidance of the pain that exists within any difficult issue. Once the pain is faced, having the ability to formulate and execute an action plan is the difference between those who retreat into "poor me" mode and those who overcome addictive behaviors.

Communication – The ability to express our feelings and communicate our needs in a way that makes it likely they can be fulfilled is also an important life skill. People who lack this level of expression are more likely to resort to overeating, in essence stuffing their feelings.

Relaxation – The ability to relax and lower one's anxiety level, independent of what technique one uses, is another important non-addictive life skill. Emotional eaters who lack one or more effective relaxation techniques use food as the means to simulate the relaxation effect.

Being Alone – The ability to enjoy one's own company has been noted as yet another life skill possessed by those likely to overcome addictive behavior. Boredom is cited as one of the top reasons for overeating. Yet as previously described, boredom is really our inability to be with ourselves. If you must constantly be entertained and find that you must be on the phone, or have the radio or TV or Internet or a video game on, food can also become your companion of choice and a means of removing you from the pleasure of your own company.

Intimate Relationships – Much of life revolves around the effort to satisfy unmet needs for intimacy and love. Scientists have documented that chocolate releases the same chemical that humans generate when we are in love. Isn't it interesting that many emotional eaters cite chocolate as the one substance they crave to deal with loneliness?

Job Skills – For many of us, what we do for a living defines our self-worth, gives meaning to our lives, and occupies a large portion of our time. It is an indisputable fact that people with a reliable way of making

133

a living, who also experience high job satisfaction, are less likely to have addictions.

Refusal Skills – Typically, a lack of strong personal boundaries and a tendency to honor unreasonable requests can lead to stuffing unwanted emotions with food. It would benefit us to stop unreasonably accommodating others, set appropriate personal boundaries and work on developing more assertive conduct when people make requests that cause us to put our best interests second. Financial generosity often masks this lack of refusal skills; we are sometimes overly generous as a result of our attempts to be accepted, to gain approval, to avoid the discomfort of having to say no.

Breaking the flow – A binge, like a nuclear bomb, is a chain reaction. It is a series of many, many thoughts that lead us to long for food and believe that food is what we need to feel better, to function, or to cope. The flow of energy builds as a longing or an obsession with a specific food to fulfill those needs. Then there is the act of putting the food into our mouths and putting in more and more. It is possible to break the flow via two alternatives. First by recognizing the lie that within food is relief, by short-circuiting the emotional roller coaster of food obsession, or by halting the grazing before it becomes a frenzy. Breaking the flow, having the ability to arrest the domino effect at any of the thought/decision junctures, is one of the critical life skills possessed by those who have overcome compulsive overeating.

Confidence – Self-confidence is a crucial factor in the ability to face the stress of life without food. When we emotional eaters lack confidence and worry that a problem may be beyond our abilities, we tend to seek refuge in food to deal with our anxieties. For those of us with self-confidence issues, it would be helpful to develop a detailed plan to increase self-esteem and the confidence in our abilities to deal with life's challenges.

Review your negative answers to the assessment at the beginning of chapter 6, and determine which of these nine life skills could be strengthened. On our site, emotionalhunger.com, there is a shortened version of this assessment that will help you pinpoint which of the nine life skills are deficient. When you identify a skill that needs work, you can formulate a plan to strengthen it. If the issue is job skills, decide what type of work brings meaning to your life and take steps to gain the necessary skill. If the issue is self-esteem, read books on the subject or attend a seminar that explores the issue. If you feel you need one-on-

one contact, seek meaningful help from friends or a professional therapist.

If you decide to seek professional counseling, you might want to begin by discussing each of these questions and asking for help in formulating a plan to bolster the respective life skills. This will lead to the self-esteem and confidence necessary to undertake this program. On our web site there is information designed to assist mental health professionals in better understanding emotional hunger and methods to help anyone interested in ending an overeating addiction.

If you honestly feel that you are ready to take the time and make the emotional investment necessary to undertake this program, let's begin the journey!

obtain the support needed

The following questions are meant to gauge some key historical background and your support infrastructure. As you answer the questions, listen to your inner wisdom and jot down ideas you might explore further to ensure your success in healing emotional hunger.

- Have you ever been diagnosed as clinically depressed? If so, is depression a chronic condition in your life? You may want to discuss the program with your mental health professional.
- Have you participated in any psychological work (seminars, self-help books, therapy) to address your weight problem?
- Have you achieved any success or insight from any of these programs? For example, have you gained understanding of the root causes of your overeating behavior?
- Do you know how to meditate? If not, are you willing to get training or take a class locally?
- Can you obtain a daily eating journal, something small that fits in your coat pocket or purse that you can carry with you at all times?
- Can you express in a journal how you feel about your weight, loneliness, anger, disappointment, taking control of your life?
- After you've written your feelings in a journal, can you verbally express these feelings to a close friend or therapist? Do you find it therapeutic to express your feelings to another person?
- If you have difficulty accessing your feelings, do you think that you would benefit from bodywork such as yoga, therapeutic massage, or Reiki, among others?

- Do you believe that it would be beneficial to feel and express emotions as they occur in your life?

step 1: self-love or self-sabotage

"To reach any significant goal, you must leave your comfort zone."
- Hyrum W. Smith

We have more than 5,000 thoughts a day. Every thought comes with a built-in attitude that either moves us to follow through with our intentions or adds to the accumulation of evidence why we should not. Every one of the prescribed steps in the "Healing Emotional Hunger" program must be undertaken with a specific attitude. If you go to the gym but while exercising you have an internal conversation that goes something like:

- "I hate exercising."
- "Other people lose weight and don't exercise."
- "Man, I look fat in these exercise clothes."
- "This is so inconvenient."
- "This takes way too much time",

you will constantly find excuses to avoid exercise or you will suffer an injury that will prevent you from exercising. Your underlying thoughts will manifest themselves whether you are taking these steps joyfully or finding reasons why you can't.

You must ask yourself two critical questions:

1. Do I have a doubtful, negative or skeptical attitude toward undertaking this program?

2. Do I need help in changing my internal self-talk to be successful during this program?

If the answer to either of these questions is yes, understand that until you address them there is very little likelihood for success. Attitude determines everything. If you need help in this area, consider reading Richard Bandler's *Using your Brain – For a Change* or watching the DVD *The Secret*.

Meditation

Self-loving talk:

- I like my life when it is stress-free.
- Meditation helps me stay with my emotions and by extension helps me stop overeating.
- Meditation helps me be present to my options, my life.
- Meditation helps me sleep soundly.
- I'm eager to love myself so much that I invest this time in me.

Self-defeating talk:

- I don't have the time to meditate.
- It's OK if I skip just one day.
- I'll do it tomorrow.
- I'll get more out of watching this TV show.
- I'm waiting for this very important phone call.
- I have to do x, y and z; I don't see where I can squeeze in meditation.
- I'm too frazzled to meditate today.

Deep Breathing

Self-loving talk:

- Wow, what a difference just 5 minutes makes!
- I'm glad I'm investing the time to slow down.
- I can really feel the difference when I do these breathing exercises.
- I can really notice the difference in how I eat when I take the "Oxygen Cocktail" before eating.
- Those "Oxygen Cocktails" really keep me from overeating.

Self-defeating talk:

- This is such bullshit!
- How can just breathing really help me stop overeating; I breathe every day.
- I don't have the time to do this.
- This is just too weird.
- This is boring.

Eat at the dinner table

Self-loving talk:	Self-defeating talk:
• I'm really enjoying setting the table for myself. • It truly helps me to eat less when I set aside the time to do so consciously. • I'm glad I'm investing time in myself. • On occasion where I have more time, I enjoy setting an elegant table where I can truly savor a gourmet meal, complete with candlelight and enjoyable music.	• I'm still going to eat the same amount whether I set the table or I eat standing up. • What?! It's just one bite from the refrigerator. • I just want to see how it tastes before deciding if I want it for dinner or not.

Checking in before eating anything

Self-loving talk:	Self-defeating talk:
• I know that just checking in helps me get in touch with my emotions and by extension not overeat. • If I don't check in I know that I'm in binge mode again.	• I don't need to check in, I'm fine, I know exactly what I'm doing. • This is silly; how is it going to help me to eat better?

Exercise

Self-loving talk:	Self-defeating talk:
• I am elated that I'm making the investment in myself. • I know all I have to do is consistently show up. • The more I do this, the better I feel and the better my body looks. • I love myself well enough to give myself this time. • I'd rather give up something else in my life, like TV or idle time, than this gift to myself. • I am investigating the most cost-effective ways for me to exercise.	• I hate exercising. • There has to be a better way to get this done. • Other people lose weight and don't exercise. • I look fat in these exercise clothes. • This is so inconvenient. • This takes way too much time. • This is too hard. • I hate to sweat. • I can't afford the membership. • I'm not seeing any changes in my body. • I don't know how to exercise. • I want to exercise but I have to take care of my family. • I can't seem to stay motivated to continue working out. • Exercise hurts. • I can't make the commitment to stick to an exercise routine.

step 2: ready to implement the plan

Because of the nature of this program, it makes more sense to set milestones than to define a rigid time frame. It will take different time periods for different individuals to achieve the same milestones. How quickly each one of us achieves these milestones depends on our individual resources:

• What is your ability to sit with your emotions?
• Where are you in your self-esteem development?

- What is your ability to turn each failure into an opportunity to learn about the underlying emotions?
- Do you feel the profound motivation to stay with the program, however long it takes?
- Do you need to develop a support infrastructure?
- How much work do you have to do to improve your physical condition?

Two important personal qualities this program requires are attitude and endurance. We need to view this enterprise as one of the most important steps we can take toward self-development, not just another diet. We need to understand that achieving these milestones will improve the quality of our lives.

milestone #1

Work up to one week of consistency before moving on:

- Meditate for at least ten minutes every day.
- Have an Oxygen Cocktail before every meal: Do two minutes of deep, slow, even breathing before each meal. Each breath should take about ten seconds, four to five seconds inhaling and four to five seconds exhaling.
- Make eating an event:
  - ➢ Eat all your meals at the dinner table. Eating at the table means not eating in the car, while standing up, directly from the refrigerator, or during other distractions.
  - ➢ Give your food your undivided attention. Your undivided attention means avoiding other activities while you are eating. No phone conversations, sorting socks, cleaning the kitchen, reading the paper, listening to the radio, or watching TV. The food has your undivided attention, and you are present to what you are eating and how you are eating.
  - ➢ Eat slowly and deliberately. Schedule sufficient time to eat. Don't rush or undervalue the importance of setting time aside to enjoy the food. Be present to what you are eating, breathe in between bites, and put the fork down while you are chewing.
  - ➢ Share meals with people who support your new lifestyle. If you enjoy going to lunch with co-workers, for example, try to choose people who do not have overeating issues of

chapter 6 – the program

their own. This is the same principle that guides recovering alcoholics to avoid drinking alcoholics. These people do not contribute nor will they support your new lifestyle.

If reading about these goals makes you anxious, journal about your feelings to get to the bottom of your anxiety.

You will need an eating journal. This could be as simple as a blank notebook in which each day has a page. Here is an example:

Date: Monday, January 11, 2010
Intention for the day: Not more than 100 grams of carbs

Plan	Actual	Emotion
Ham & cheese Omelet – 5 carb grams	3 Donuts – 105 carb grams	Stressed out after a tense meeting, felt anxious

Each daily page is divided into three columns. In column one, write your eating plan. An eating plan enables you to formulate a conscientious but realistic plan detailing what you are going to eat. The first column details your plan for breakfast, snack, lunch, snack, dinner, and late snack. Column two contains what you actually eat and column three contains what feelings you experience only if you deviate from your plans. If you substitute a food and the substitution has the same value, you are still within your eating goals. What is important is that you have met your intent.

Make a seven-day eating plan that is right for you.

If you deviate from your eating plan, write down how you felt every time. Write about why you deviated from your eating plan. Write down any significant emotion – for example anxiety or disappointment – that arises when you deviate from your eating plan.
Before eating anything – anything at all – that is not in your eating plan, breathe for at least one minute and ask yourself how you're feeling. What is going on internally? What is being suppressed?
During this training period, omit anything from your life that makes you feel inadequate or anxious. This will probably include fashion magazines, TV programs with many eating messages, visits to friends

and family that cause emotional distress, and any other situation that you know makes you anxious.

Do at least one hour per week of physical exercise that matches and challenges your fitness level. If all you can do is walk for twenty minutes three times a week, start there.

milestone #2

Work up to one week of consistency before moving on:

- Meditate for at least 10 minutes every day
- Do three two-minute deep breathing exercises
- Make a commitment to eat all your meals at the dinner table
- Generate a nurturing seven-day eating plan. Plan healthy, enjoyable meals for yourself. Plan the portions that you will eat. Decide how you are going to gauge* whether you are eating the portions you wanted to eat
- Before eating anything – anything at all – breathe for at least two minutes and ask yourself how you are feeling. What is going on internally? What is being suppressed?
- Write down in your journal any significant emotion, such as anxiety, disappointment and so on, when you deviate from your eating plan
- Omit anything that makes you feel inadequate: fashion magazines, TV programs, visits to friends and family that cause you stress, or newspapers if you find that the news causes a change in your mood and emotions
- Do at least an hour and a half per week of physical exercise that matches and challenges your fitness level

* If you are fortunate enough to be able to cook for yourself, you might want to invest in a good scale and have all the appropriate measuring utensils to ensure that you are cooking appropriate portions. Many of the recipes that I attempted had a serving size of four. I cooked the entire portion, always telling myself that I would put the three other servings in the refrigerator for a later time. Of course it didn't work that way. I usually ate two servings or the entire four servings. You know what I'm talking about. I recommend that you prepare only one serving until you learn the joy of eating only one serving. Alternatively, buy a cookbook that fits your situation. A large percentage of our population is single, so there is a variety of cookbooks available that support cooking for one or two. Even cooking utensils are marketed to the

single lifestyle, and things like miniature crock pots are now available that make it easier to cook for one person.

milestone #3

Work up to one week of consistency before moving on:
- Meditate at least 15 minutes every day.
- Do four five-minute deep breathing exercises.
- Generate your own personal, nurturing, seven-day eating plan.
- Successfully meet your eating plan four days out of seven. For example, if your goal is to eat only 100 grams of carbohydrates daily, if you have achieve that objective four days out of seven, you are within the plan.
- Demonstrate the ability to sit with your emotions 25 percent of the time.
- Journal about your feelings every time you experience emotional hunger.
- Before eating anything – anything at all – breathe for at least 2 minutes and ask yourself, "How am I feeling? Are any emotions being suppressed? How is my anxiety level?"
- Write in your journal about any significant emotion – anxiety, disappointment or any others – when you deviate from your eating plan.
- List the things that make you feel inadequate – fashion magazines, TV programs, visits to friends and family, newspapers – and acknowledge that you don't need these in your life.
- Do at least two hours per week of physical exercise that matches your fitness level.

milestone #4

- Meditate at least 20 minutes every day.
- Do four five-minute deep breathing exercises.
- Generate a nurturing seven-day eating plan.
- Successfully meet your eating plan six days out of seven.
- Demonstrate the ability to sit with your emotions 75 percent of the time.
- Journal about your feelings every time you experience emotional hunger.

- Before eating anything – anything at all – ask yourself how you are feeling. What is going on internally? Check in with your body and feel whether anything is being suppressed.
- Write in your journal any significant emotion – anxiety, disappointment or any others – when you deviate from your eating plan.
- Omit anything that makes you feel inadequate: fashion magazines, TV programs, visits to friends and family, newspapers, etc.
- Do at least two-and-a-half hours per week of physical exercise that matches your fitness level.

forming a new relationship with food

When you authentically embrace the essence of The End of Diets program, there is no need for a diet as such, for you understand that food is not the automatic response to the ups and downs of life, nor is food an obsession, a reward, or a way to deal with your emotions. Once food is seen as nutrition and ceases to be a coping mechanism to soothe the discomfort of your emotions, once you are driven by self-love instead of suppressing your emotions, there will be no need for a diet. Then you can decide what to eat based on what sounds pleasurable or what is nutritionally good for you. Your body will start craving specific things such as more vegetables, more water, more protein, or more fruit. The wisdom of your body will guide you to what you need.

I recognize that this may not have happened by the time you reach this page. The healing of emotional hunger, and the power of that healing to transform your life, is not a matter of acquiring information but of experiencing self-love and feeling your emotions as they translate into body sensations. Then it is a matter of being with your emotions until they dissipate and stop manifesting as emotional hunger. How long will it take to achieve these significant personal transformations? It depends on your life skills, your personal resiliency and tenacity, and how much emotional blockage is stored in your body. Until all these breakthroughs occur in your life, the concept of having the body wisdom to choose foods out of self-love is only that –a concept printed in words.

If you have to lose 50, 100, 200 or more pounds until you gain the gift of self-love, an unblocked emotional body, access to your emotions,

chapter 6 – the program

and a quiet mind, what should you eat? Let's examine the three most popular nutritional philosophies.

First I must warn you that each of these has a compelling arsenal of studies, anecdotes, poster children, and an M.D. or six who will vouch for its validity. Author and food editor Fran McCullough expresses it best when she says, "One of the problems with diet books is that the authors always insist theirs is the only way, the one truth that solves all mysteries that have heretofore baffled mankind. Obviously they can't all be right, and sorting out which elements of which ones are right for you can be a full-time job.[10]"

I recently found a quote that stated that nutrition is the least understood of all sciences. Choose a plan that feels appropriate for your current condition – one that does not bring up massive resistance from your psyche and with which you can experience consistent results so you don't get discouraged. The plan you choose may need to be revamped in three to six months, either because it has lost its effectiveness or because you've simply become bored with it and need a change.

At this stage you can minimally short-circuit the automatic response to eating whenever you feel any emotional discomfort and breathe with healing intention as you stay tuned to the sensations of your body. Your body WILL sense when things aren't working with your nutritional strategy. Having access to those telling sensations is a matter of being attuned. Some claim it's having enough silence in your life that you can listen to the small voice inside and give yourself the time to experience the feelings that arise.

the low-calorie/natural foods philosophy

The consensus of this camp is to eat small, balanced meals, or what I used to call a snack, when emotional eating dictated my food portions. Meals consist mostly of vegetables, plenty of fruit and fish, lean white meats, and essentially no red meat or hydrogenated oils, and only whole grain, high fiber, unprocessed carbohydrates (which means no white sugar, white rice, or white pasta). The underlying philosophy of this camp is that any food that has been tampered with via chemicals, restrictive animal treatment, radiation or hormone injection will affect you adversely sooner or later. All prepared food should contain no chemical preservatives. Eggs should come from free-range chickens, and everything should be as natural as possible. Vegetables should be organic, and the drink of choice is generous amounts of pure water.

Most good health food stores have a nutritionist on staff or a list from which they can recommend a nutritionist who can help you eat in this manner.

the low-fat philosophy

There are currently 1,457 books available on amazon.com under the selected topic "low fat." At least 20% of all products in the supermarket are advertised as low fat. Unfortunately, many of these same products are high in refined carbohydrates. Most Americans who are attempting to lose weight seem to be on one version or another of a low-fat diet. The low-fat philosophy explains why fats are not good for us, and which types of fats we should avoid. Each type of fat has a different effect on the body. Sorry to say, the majority of these effects are not good for you. Most researchers say that only two types of fat are good for us, and they are beneficial only when eaten in moderation. Here is a simple breakdown.

Saturated fats are solids at room temperature but become liquid when heated. Most saturated fats are animal in origin and come from meat, poultry, and dairy products. Limit your intake of saturated fat as much as possible. Saturated fats raise cholesterol and triglyceride levels, and some research shows that they seem to interfere with immune functioning. Two vegetable sources you should watch are coconut oil and palm kernel oil, which are high in saturated fat even though they're plant oils.

Polyunsaturated fats originate from plant sources and are liquid at room temperature. They are considered to be a "healthier" fat because they help lower total cholesterol and triglyceride levels. Vegetable oils such as safflower, sunflower, sesame, cottonseed and corn oil are polyunsaturated fats.

Monounsaturated fats include olive oil, canola, and peanut oil. Oils that are high in monounsaturated fats are the "healthiest" choices because they help decrease the low-density lipoprotein (LDL) levels, or "bad" cholesterol.

Hydrogenated fats, also known as trans-fats, begin as liquid fats but are solidified when hydrogen atoms are added. A healthy or unsaturated fat is thereby converted into an unhealthy or saturated fat. You may be asking yourself why anyone would do such a thing. Hydrogenated oils are cheaper and extend the shelf life of packaged foods. The oil is less

chapter 6 – the program

likely to break down over time and become rancid. Most of the hydrogenated fats we eat come from partially hydrogenated vegetable oils, which are found in packaged foods. Take a look at the labels on cookies, crackers, sauces, margarines, shortening and peanut butter. Before you buy it and eat it, read it!

I'm not a nutritionist, but after trying many of these low fat approaches, my recommendation from this camp is Dr. Dean Ornish's Program for *Reversing Heart Disease*. Dr. Ornish's book contains 150 recipes. In addition, Dr. Ornish also has two cookbooks that support his findings and research: *Eat More, Weigh Less*: *Dr. Dean Ornish's Life Choice Program for Losing Weight Safely While Eating Abundantly* and *Everyday Cooking with Dr. Dean Ornish: 150 Easy, Low-Fat, High-Flavor Recipes*. I'm sure many of you are probably thinking, "I don't have a heart problem, I just need to lose weight." Once again, there are 1,457 books on the topic of low fat, and Dr. Ornish's philosophy is the one I would recommend if low fat is what speaks to you. Obviously, if you find Dr. Ornish's approach totally unsuitable but you still want to pursue a low-fat approach, there are countless other interpretations of what a low-fat philosophy is and how it will help you lose weight.

the low carb/low sugar philosophy

The basic objective of this camp is to change the way our bodies fuel themselves. Our bodies use the nutrients contained in food in the following order:

- Carbohydrates
- Fat
- Protein

With low fat and low calorie diets, you are not burning fat until you've used up all your carbohydrates. If you're eating carbohydrates, you will be burning those carbohydrates and not fat for energy. When you eat foods high in carbohydrates – those that contain starch or sugar – your body breaks them all down into the same thing: glucose. To simplify, one could say that your body barely knows the difference between a potato, white rice, and a soft drink, although the potato is much healthier since it contains more vitamins and minerals. Once the carbohydrates have been broken down, the glucose enters the bloodstream and signals the release of insulin. Insulin changes the glucose into glycogen, which is then moved into the liver and cells where it is stored for energy use. When these sites are full and there is still glucose in the bloodstream, insulin changes the excess glucose into triglycerides. Triglycerides are fat. They are moved to your adipose tissue – your body's fat stores.

The intent of the low-carbohydrate diet is to switch your body from a carbohydrate-burning engine to a fat-burning engine. Because you're not eating many carbohydrates (which by the way turn to sugar and fat in the body), your body will have no choice but to burn fat.

I must warn you, however, that if you choose one of the low carb/low sugar eating modalities, the first week might be pure hell as your body goes through carbohydrate withdrawal. Some people find the low carb approach appealing because they can eat all types of meat, cheese, vegetables, cream, fatty fish (such as salmon), bacon and eggs, cheeseburgers (without the bread, of course) and on and on...hence the popularity of this approach. Some people report a sense of satisfaction. You do feel full. Emotional overeaters who rely on carbohydrates typically consume 500 to 800 g of carbs a day. In contrast, the low carb/low sugar diet requires that we eat only 20 g of carbohydrates per day in the first two weeks. Making this drastic reduction of carbohydrates in an effort to burn fat might adversely affect your mood and energy level. Here is a captivatingly funny account from an Irishman, M. Sutherland, regarding his first week's experience with the most famous of all the low carb/low sugar approaches, the Atkins diet:

"When I stood on the scale this morning it hit 73kg (160 lbs.) right on the nose. Before I started the diet last week I was at 77 (169 lbs.) That's 4kg in one week. Whatever else you can say about Atkins, the only other times I have lost that much weight that quickly are when I've been stuck in bed with Scottish Barfing Syndrome (SBS) and unable to eat anything at all.

But not even that kind of weight loss can make up for the fact that this diet is making me utterly miserable. I've learned that for me, the pleasure I derive from food resides in carbohydrates. By cutting out the carbs, I've cut out my joy.

After a meal I feel full but never satisfied. Before meal times I don't feel hungry, I feel nauseous. The thought of having to eat meat turns my stomach. Intellectually I know that's partly a low blood sugar kind of thing. I know that I'll feel much better after I've forced myself to eat something. But at the time I really do have to force myself to cook, or to sit down to eat. For all the enjoyment I get from a nice chunk of beef

chapter 6 – the program

or a succulent roast chicken, I might as well be scarfing down those multicolored protein cubes you got in 70s science fiction films. They're just about as appetizing.

As I was walking by the bakery section in Safeway on Friday, I almost lost it. I had to suppress a hysterical giggle bubbling up inside of me. I had visions of running over to the fresh bread counter, ripping the crust off a large bloomer and burying my face in the soft, warm expanse of white loaf. Then I'd take my clothes off and rub the crust all over my naked body just to see if I could absorb any more carbohydrates through my pores.

To summarize: Atkins is effective for me, and I'll keep it up for the second week of the "induction phase" (20g carb/day) on the off-chance that my body is just taking a long time to adjust to the new balance of nutrients, but I really don't like it. It doesn't feel like a diet, it feels like punishment. On a calorie-controlled diet (1500kCal/day) I do feel hungry, but the hunger feels virtuous. It doesn't make me miserable. We'll see how it goes, but a week from now it may be time to switch."[9]

My recommendation is that if you are going to try low carb eating, you should read Fran McCullough's *Living Low Carb*[10], which starts with a survey of the various schools of thought and then gives you hundreds of recipes you can use to support this lifestyle.

Once again, these are not diets so much as eating philosophies that you adopt for the long term. Once you are no longer driven by your suppressed emotions, you will not be surprised to find that you can stay on an eating regimen for the rest of your life.

Millions of people have lost weight once they settled into one of these three popular approaches. Most people lose weight when they become aware of how many calories, or fat grams or carb grams they are consuming per day and consistently adhere to a healthy routine over a period of several weeks or months. Please be aware that the critical behaviors are awareness and honesty. I remember being unaware that I was eating specific foods and having to write down everything I ate in order to know what I was truly consuming. Then I began to play games. I told myself that a specific food had only so many calories, or fat or carb grams when in reality the food had substantially more value than I wanted to assign it. If you are diligent and honest about your consumption, which for most of us means writing everything down, you will lose weight.

You must choose an approach that works for you, that allows you to lose some body fat consistently and, more importantly, an approach that you can live with for the rest of your life. Having said that, you might have to experiment with several approaches before you settle on one. Then comes the true breakthrough: The End of Diets program your weight loss will be permanent. Unlike 97% of dieters who regain the weight they've worked so hard to lose, you will succeed because you will have ceased using food as a means of coping with life. This time the weight will stay off.

crossing the bridge

Hopefully by the time you read this section you will have gained substantial understanding about the causes of emotional hunger and glimpsed the possibilities of healing emotional hunger. But the reality exists of understanding the addiction and gaining the life skills to eradicate it. As I mentioned in previous chapters understanding is not healing, just as a bandage is not new skin. The life skills needed to eradicate the addiction cannot be acquired as a matter of will. All skills are acquired through practice and mindfulness. While we cross this bridge here are some aids - bread for the journey, if you will.

Take up the art of healing breathing – By now you understand that any emotional imbalance will inexplicably cause emotional hunger. It is for many of us a conditioned reflex, no different than when a doctor hits your knee with a mallet and the leg kicks forward. If you remember the "wax on, wax off" scenes from The Karate Kid you've seen how we can develop desirable conditioned reflexes. Mr. Miyagi was training Daniel so his muscles would instantly respond with precise defensive movements without having to stop and think. Likewise we need to develop deep breathing as a conditioned reflex. This will become our first line of defense against compulsive and mindless eating. When emotional hunger kicks in we must take several deep healing breaths to break the flow that leads us to unconscious eating. For those of us who spend endless hours in front of a computer, there is a useful freeware program that will chime every 20 minutes as a reminder to take those healing breaths. Each time we stop and breathe, we reinforce the reflex that will help us interrupt the flow of the emotional hunger. You can download this wonderful aid from www.mindfulnessdc.org/mindfulclock.html.

chapter 6 – the program

Eating journal – Make yourself write down everything you eat. Acknowledge when you've had a satisfying meal, i.e., a meal that satisfied your physical requirements for nourishment and your human need for pleasure. Be cognizant that emotional overeating is unconscious eating. By being present and heightening the awareness of what we actually did eat, it is more difficult to deny when our hunger is emotional and not physical in nature.

Keep meals pleasurable – Be mindful that for many of us eating IS our daily pleasure. Until you learn to satisfy that basic human need for pleasure from other sources, make sure that there is pleasure in eating. But be aware that this doesn't mean a binge. It means simply that you are counting on your meal being pleasurable. If you deny this need, you are likely to sabotage your good intentions with a disproportionate response, such as a binge. As we have already discussed, slow down, enjoy each bite consciously. Put your fork down between bites. Breathe.

Meditate – Find a teacher, a guru, a meditation group, whatever you have to do to learn this critical life skill. Just do it! This will be the most profound tool you will possess in your arsenal toward eradicating compulsive overeating. It might be the most challenging, but in the end it will be the most life enhancing.

Use the "Break the Flow" skill – The moment you begin thinking, longing, fantasizing about food you must break the flow. You can physically or mentally yell NOOOOOOOOO! or instead use the emotional hunger as an opportunity to give thanks for the movement, vitality, joy, and exuberance of your new, healthy body. Use powerful intentions and visualization of what you genuinely want in your life. One useful tool is Neuro-Linguistic Programming (NLP). Anchor the conditioned reflex of emotional hunger as the trigger to roll the movie, the emotional experience of what it is that you want.

Learn from setbacks – Be compassionate and patient with yourself when you do experience a setback. The mantra becomes "What is it that I'm supposed to learn from this? I'm open, ready and able to receive the lesson." Journal whenever setbacks occur. These are your greatest opportunities for self-discovery. What are the triggering points, what is it that needs to be healed?

what should I eat?

At the beginning, faithfully record whatever you decide you are going to track, be it fat grams, grams of carbohydrates, calories, air molecules ☺. Be mindful, persistent and diligent about writing down and tallying whatever you consume. As long as you become conscious of what you are eating – by writing it down and acknowledging it on an emotional level – you can honor your inner wisdom that leads you to choose your food wisely.

I believe that each camp - low fat, low carb, and whole food – has some truth. I've compiled my own version of which foods best serve my interests. But because the question "What should I eat?" arises at every single discussion of this book, my recommendation is to read or listen to *Eating Well for Optimum Health* by Andrew Weil, MD. In his book Dr. Weil provides a comprehensive overview of the eating camps, which helped me realize that no one has the truth cornered.

You can combine the excellent information on nutrition with behavior modification techniques that will help you be with your emotions and eat consciously. For example, a personal goal of mine is to be with the hunger after 8 PM. In the beginning this was excruciatingly difficult because I have used food as a relax aid and sleeping pill for so many years. This discomfort became another opportunity to use breathing and journaling extensively.

7 - learning to love the plateau

"Lord, give me the determination and the tenacity of a weed."

– R. Walters

In his book *Mastery*, George Leonard describes that in learning any new skill there are three types of personalities — the dabbler, the compulsive and the master. The dabbler is the person who practices a new skill until she reaches a comfortable level of proficiency, called a plateau. But after reaching a plateau, the dabbler will stay it for the rest of her life. The compulsive is one who approaches a new skill at 1,000% intensity, giving it her all, life and soul, completely focusing on achieving this new skill. Her enthusiasm is fierce, and her progress is all over the map, reaching the plateau faster than other participants, but somehow quickly losing her proficiency. Soon after the compulsive undertakes a new skill, she finds a compelling reason why she can not pursue it - for example getting injured - and then moves onto yet another new compulsion.

The master is the person who learns to love the plateau, the person who loves the performance of the new skill. She is the person who can practice the guitar for hours, seeking to master the instrument but never becoming addicted to having progress happen NOW. The master's approach involves slow and steady practice for the simple pleasure of the practice itself. In order for anyone to master anything, according to Leonard's theory - relationship, tennis, playing an instrument, being a good mother - one must love the practice, that plateau where progress is not perceptible.

Healing emotional hunger is a process of learning new skills, and those who master them learn to love the practice even when the scale doesn't move for weeks. These individuals are on a journey of self-discovery and, and they learn to love the journey for its own sake.

On all important journeys, there are many useful tools we can take with us. The most important is tenacity: be as tenacious as a weed so that nothing deters you from your vision of health. This journey will be as long as your personal development requires. Imagine that you are traveling from the United States to the tip of South America, Tierra del Fuego, Argentina. You are excited about your trip and the many wonderful things you are going to discover and experience. But you must plan. You decide what to pack – what is essential and what is optional. When your trip begins you are delighted, you are ready.

If you choose to drive – and yes there are people who have driven there – little by little, week by week, day by day, you continue. Soon the first excitement wears thin, and still you drive. The trip will be a world-class adventure for those who learn to experience each day for what it is. If your choice is to drive you must learn how to love the road.

And so with us: There are going to be many weeks when the sense of how much we are working versus the results we see on the scale, in the mirror, in our clothes might seem negligible. Then the lack of perceived progress leads to frustration which, if not processed, leads to overeating. Once the excitement and the newness subside, we can easily relapse into the dysfunctional behavior of overeating or talk ourselves into giving up the goals we've set.

If our decision is to reach our destination, we must plan how to get through these many weeks while the marketed hype of overnight weight loss and the reality of our incremental progress are quite obviously out of sync. We must plan to be bored, to be disenchanted, to want to quit and not endure another day feeling the many emotions we have to face to see this journey through. The essential attitude is to celebrate small progress – to understand and be enthusiastic about one pound a week because it adds up to 50 pounds a year – two pounds a week to 100 pounds a year. And because these are pounds released through self-love, by being present with our emotions, they are pounds that are not coming back. We must learn to appreciate small progress versus the delusion of ten pounds a week. That is the key to transformation and to lifelong success.

affirmations

The first tool we are going to discuss is affirmation. Affirmations are powerful aids. Unfortunately, as with most powerful tools, their use has been applied to situations in which they do not provide significant benefit. As an emotional eater, it is ineffective to use affirmations to "change" your feelings. Once we understand the distinctions between the function of the mind and the nature of emotions, we can begin applying affirmations correctly. For example, if you are depressed, no amount of affirmation will make you feel better. You cannot talk yourself out of your emotions; you cannot affirm yourself out of your feelings. Disappointment is a feeling; affirmation is an alternative

chapter 7 – learning to love the plateau

frame of mind, a counter to a judgment we have made. Affirmations can be used effectively to counter judgments. They will do little or nothing to change feelings.

For most emotional eaters one prevalent and self-defeating habit is the abuse to which we subject ourselves on a daily basis. There is constant chatter in our minds that we are not thin enough, not good enough, not pretty enough, not worth loving. These are all judgments based on a value system that reflects our society's current beauty standards, and unfortunately we have come to accept many of these values as our own.

For the longest time I could not accept myself as a FAT woman. This lack of self-acceptance contributed to my inability to be in touch with my body. I wrongly believed that embracing and accepting myself as a FAT woman ran counter to my desire to overcome my food addiction. I believed that if I was at peace with my FAT body, I was in fact raising the white flag of surrender to overeating. There seemed no way to reconcile the disparity.

Anything that is a judgment, and consequently a by-product generated by the mind, can be countered with affirmations. The more persistent and powerful the affirmation, the more likely the affirmation will counter the automatic judgments of our programming.

Any time we use an affirmation to counter our feelings we are in fact rejecting our emotions, and by extension rejecting ourselves. Be very, very clear on the distinction. Honor and accept your feelings AND use affirmations to eradicate JUDGMENTS that don't serve you.

effective affirmations:

- I honor and accept all my emotions
- I trust the wisdom of my body
- I'm grateful for my body
- I'm grateful for the problem-solving abilities of my mind
- I am worthy of love and respect exactly as I am
- My self-worth is created by my self-talk and judgments
- My self-worth is independent of how I compare with others
- I accept myself exactly as I am
- I am a beautiful person because of my divine nature

These affirmations directly counter negative judgments about ourselves. They do not attempt to change our feelings. They only attempt to counter-balance the negative judgments that are constantly generated by our minds.

ineffective affirmations:

If you glance at the list of positive affirmations that you just read, you will see that they are short and simple. Each one seeks to counteract, purely and powerfully as it is repeated, a negative, habitual judgment, much like repeating a mantra. The primary rule for affirmations, then, is "keep it simple and positive." The affirmations below are not effective for two reasons: They try to effect emotions as well as judgments, and they try to do too much.

I am worthy and will be loved even when a man doesn't find me attractive. You cannot dictate the emotions of others nor can you affect the future with affirmations. Affirmations can help only in countering the judgments of your mind. This affirmation still focuses on the negative judgment of unattractiveness.

I am worthy of love and respect, even when I feel weak or needy. Because of the clause "when I feel weak or needy," we are still indirectly trying to influence the realm of our emotions. Affirmations cannot change your emotions; they can only help in countering the judgments of your mind.

My self-worth is totally independent of whether others agree with me or are satisfied with me. Again, the only thing we can affirm against are our self-judgments, not the agreement or satisfaction of others. So the clause, "Others agree," clouds the effectiveness of the affirmation. Stay within the realm of personal judgments.

I deserve love and respect even when I need to say "No" and feel badly because I can't comply with the demands of others. For many of us saying "No" brings feelings of guilt because we have been taught to always be accommodating of others. This affirmation could be restated as "I deserve love and respect." Once again, we can't affirm away our emotions.

I accept and love myself as I am, with my faults and weakness, as I steadily and methodically evolve out of them. Great intent, but affirmations can only help in countering the judgments of mind. We must accept that we will have feelings of inadequacy and embrace those feelings as normal.

visualization

After reading about visualization, I understood that it was a very powerful tool. I attempted to visualize myself thin, wearing the clothes that I wanted to wear and doing all the activities I wanted to do. Somehow these visualizations very difficult, so I stopped the visualization business.

For me, visualization became a breakthrough when I used it as a means of changing behaviors that would make a difference in my healing. I started visualizing effectively when I used it during my most vulnerable time of the day, which was between 7:30 and 11 P.M. If I was alone at home, this was my lonely time. If my son was at home, this was TV time. Both loneliness and TV time meant overeating. In either case, this was the time that I needed to be careful. When I began to set aside 7 to 7:15 P.M. to visualize what I wanted in my life, my progress catapulted to the next level.

First, I began visualizing being in touch with my emotions, eating very specific foods, doing yoga, meditating, or running on my treadmill. In other words, I visualized engaging in the behaviors that would help me achieve my health objectives. I did not visualize being thin because that was still difficult for me. However, the miracle happened when behaviors that helped me become fit changed my mind and I began to believe that I could be thin. Then the visualization evolved into what my life would be like when I was thin. Then I began visualizing being fit and trim, wearing shorts, jeans, elegant gowns, swimsuits, smart business suits, and jazzy evening outfits. Then it became possible to visualize doing anything I wanted – biking, hiking, skiing, dancing, or going to the public swimming pool.

Finally, my visualizations evolved into the most powerful of all, living from the life force, with total freedom of movement, having a life not limited by my body, being open and accepting, being vital and energetic even while doing the simple tasks of life, and being happy and proud of my body. That was astounding – a new drug for me – and I wanted that 'addiction' for life. Visualizations became powerful intentions, not just physical feelings; they acquired a sense of destiny versus being just wishes.

The lesson in this story is that if you want to employ this type of energy shift in your life, start by visualizing things within your belief system.

As soon as you see progress, you are ready to move to the next level to begin manifesting the power of intention.

effective visualization

- First relax into a deep, quiet, meditative state of mind
- Keep "seeing" the intention until you feel it – the stronger the feeling the more effective the visualization
- Be as specific and as detailed as possible: use all of your sense
- Feel the preparation, the surroundings, the sounds, the taste, how your body shifts, how it moves, your enthusiasm in doing the activity

For visualization to really work, you not only have to see what it is you want to achieve, it also has to be within your belief system. The difference between idle daydreaming and effective visualization practice is the knowingness, the belief, the trust that our visualization, our desires are possible. If our beliefs counter our desires, it is very difficult to get past the wall of these beliefs to the possibility of realizing our desires. Effective visualization occurs only when you feel a sense of confidence that what you are imagining will actually come to pass.

Effective visualization is accompanied by strong emotions and sensations. You experience bodily signals, hear surrounding sounds, in essence have the same physical sensations as when you are actually engaging in the activity or experiencing the event. You must have an emotional shift and experience the joy of what you want. You transport your consciousness to the realm of pure feeling. Don't just say the words in your mind if you cannot experience, at a minimum, a shift in your emotional energies; the visualization will not produce any change without the emotional component.

Another important aspect of visualization is to understand that as with any skill, the more you practice it, the better you will become. That is why always, but especially when you begin this practice, you should attempt to visualize only the things that are within your belief system. Then practice the visualizations until you feel them at such a level that there is no question in your body about the reality of the event. As you make progress, evolve the visualization into the next level, allow it to deepen in detail and feeling, but base it on the progress that you have achieved.

chapter 7 – learning to love the plateau

stage 1

- Visualize ten cleansing breaths before each meal
- Visualize observing whatever emotions might come up before your meal
- Visualize breathing into any discomfort or anxiety
- Visualize that you keep on breathing with the intention of processing these emotions before eating
- Visualize stopping the breathing process only when the emotional energies shift
- Visualize eating calmly and intentionally while thoroughly enjoying your food

visualize going to yoga three times a week

- Visualize packing the yoga outfit the night before the class.
- Feel yourself doing each move.
- If you know the specific poses of the program, write down something about each move. For example, my practice begins with 60 cleansing breaths, followed by the half moon posture. The half moon posture requires letting go of the anxiety that I feel when I pull my body into an awkward position with a calm, quiet mind. I can visualize my body bending and being aware only of my breath as it pulls.
- Visualize the sweat as your body begins giving weight to these moves.
- Feel excited as you anticipate doing all of the moves
- Feel each move making muscles elongate
- Feel the energy in the room
- Feel the kinks in your neck loosen
- Feel the stress between your shoulders evaporating
- Feel the benefits of being supple, stress-free and toned

visualize running one... two... five miles

The point is not to fret that "Oh my God, I can't run five miles!" When I began this visualization I understood that I couldn't even walk one mile on the treadmill, let alone run five miles. However, I did believe with all of my heart, with enthusiasm and elation, that if I stuck with this exercise program, one day I would be able to run five miles. I knew that instinctively, profoundly, from a Noetic sense. At the beginning all I could do was walk one mile, but slowly I was able to increase the duration and intensity. I would typically schedule only three miles in one day. But somehow the five-mile mark always came back, and I knew I could do it. I kept visualizing running the five miles, and this visualization turned into doing two sessions of 2.5 miles per day. Then it became three miles in the morning and two miles at night. Then 3.5, then 4.5, until one day I was able to do all five miles in one continuous session. I was elated! That had been my goal for many years.

The point is to visualize running that first mile, then the second, and on until you reach your goal. That visualization by itself will encourage and facilitate progress. It helped me get onto the treadmill, too, and as most of us know, just starting is the most difficult part.

- Feel your breath
- Feel getting into the rhythm of the pace
- Feel the sweat

visualize eating life-nourishing foods

- Visualize planning good meals for yourself
- Visualize going shopping for life-nourishing ingredients
- Visualize cooking life-nourishing food
- Visualize setting the table as though a good friend were coming over
- Visualize enjoying the food and being present to the joy of eating well
- Visualize eating only until you feel vital and light and never bloated
- Visualize celebrating that you are taking care of you
- Visualize having contingency plans for impromptu invitations to eat out
- Visualize never spending more than $20 per meal when eating out. (This is not about saving money; for me having a $20 budget made me choose carefully what I ordered. So the budgetary restriction was yet another aid in ensuring that I would not order everything on the menu.)

visualize meditating each day for 15 minutes

- Visualize setting the time to meditate as you plan your day.

chapter 7 – learning to love the plateau

- Visualize selecting an alternative time if external forces influence you to change your schedule
- Visualize getting into the rhythm of meditation
- Visualize the gift of a calm and relaxed mind
- Visualize the gift of having access to your body's wisdom
- Visualize living free of stress
- Visualize being able to enjoy all the beauty of life
- Visualize being in touch with your emotions
- Visualize being able to sit with whatever comes up
- Visualize yourself being aware of the emotional hunger and immediately knowing that you need to turn inside to find out what is happening within
- Visualize sitting with yourself, breathing, searching your body, and asking, "What is fueling the hunger? What do I need?"
- Visualize finding the emotion and sitting with it – without judgment, without problem-solving – just being with it compassionately and with an accepting heart
- Visualize being patient in bringing the emotion into consciousness
- Visualize holding the emotion in consciousness lovingly until it dissipates

stage 2

visualize being fit and trim

- Experience the joy of feeling light and free
- Be ecstatic about your freedom of movement
- Be excited about your amazing range of motion
- Feel vital, energetic, and alive
- Feel toned and glowing with health
- Feel beautiful, at ease, elegant, breezy. See yourself wearing shorts, sexy jeans, beautiful gowns, swimsuits, smart business suits and elegant evening outfits
- Feel sexy wearing a sleeveless, black cocktail dress
- Embrace your beauty, your glow, the sensuality of your shoulders in that black cocktail dress
- Be the joy of movement and freedom in wearing such an outfit
- Feel the sense of pride in being comfortable in your own skin

- Be energized by doing anything you want – biking, hiking, skiing, dancing
- FEEL the childlike fun of these activities
- Radiate the sense of discovery and awe as you hike into nature's beauty
- Experience the exhilaration of moving with music
- TASTE the delight of biking up that mountain, or facing that downhill slope, or biking all day long, or dancing all night long
- BE in that moment where you meet whomever you want
- Feel the joy of getting to know that special person you always wanted to meet
- Exult in the compliment given to you by someone in whom you are interested
- Feel confident as you get to know that person
- Feel that person look into your eyes, knowing s/he is interested in you

stage 3

- feel loving yourself truly and unconditionally
- Feel being in touch with the needs that are really important for you
- Feel putting these needs ahead of everything and everyone else
- Feel kindness and compassion towards yourself
- Feel taking care of yourself and being your very best friend
- Feel accepting of all of your emotions
- Experience having a healthy and vibrant self-esteem
- Become aware of your physical and energetic humanity and scheduling time for nurturing relaxation and recreation
- Honor your patience, generosity, forgiveness, and self-respect
- Honor your physical needs, obtain appropriate medical care, and always making time for your physical fitness, meditation, and bodywork
- Experience openness when love knocks at your door
- Feel the energy of living your life with vitality and stamina.
- Experience the energy to do whatever you want˙
- Have the enthusiasm for doing new projects
- Live with exuberance and embrace the quality of your life
- Live on a daily basis from the life force, vital and fully alive

chapter 7 – learning to love the plateau

- Be in a state of grace and feel thankful for all your blessings

Visualization is a powerful tool to help us keep on track. By now you probably understand that this is not a lose-ten-pounds-in-two-days nonsense diet; this is a life-altering transformation. Not only will you lose weight, but more importantly, that weight will stay off because this method is not a fad. It is a change of behavior and attitude.

Visualization is important because we all need to stay enthusiastic and focused on the long-term journey. Visualization was a key in helping me keep my long-term goal alive. More importantly, it helped me reach certain goals I might never have attained had I not visualized going to yoga three times a week, getting on the treadmill and running five miles, and not putting food in my mouth while watching TV.

the law of attraction

In recent years literature and belief systems have emerged in the area that I will term Emotional Energy (EE). The most recognizable books in this category are:

- *Think and Grow Rich* by Napoleon Hill
- *How to Win Friends & Influence People* by Dale Carnegie
- *Creative Visualization* by Shakti Gawain

The concept of EE has recently been made more accessible by movies such as *What the Bleep do We Know?* and the *The Secret*. The message of these movies is that there is a scientific explanation for why some people manifest what they want in their lives, while others, despite wanting the same things, do not. In these movies scientists and New Thought gurus explain why we attract what we think about most - not what we want the most but what we invest emotional energy in. Be it positive or negative, whatever we hold in our consciousness with enough emotional energy is what manifests in our life. This explains why the time we agonize over, desire, or long for food and how terrified we are about not being socially acceptable contributes to our state of perpetual dieting. Instead we should invest our Emotional Energy in being grateful that we've reached our ideal weight. Obviously many of us are going to ask: "How can I put emotional energy into being grateful for something that has not occurred?" If these scientists are correct many of us have manifested a reality of perpetual dieting and chronic self-hate precisely because we don't understand, and therefore incorrectly practice, the Law of Attraction.

Once we know that energy, in the form of thoughts and emotions, becomes our reality, we begin to understand that because we have spent so much time dreaming of, longing for, wanting, and desiring food, we have no choice but to spend a corresponding amount of energy manifesting those thoughts into the action of eating. Another time-consuming thought pattern is the self-hate cycle of "I'm too FAT," "I look unattractive in ALL of my clothes," or "I'll never find a person who loves me." Whatever the self-hating cycle, those thoughts translate into self-sabotaging activities such as not exercising and not putting a priority on activities that contribute to our growth, joy, enthusiasm, and vitality.

The universe is transformed energy; thoughts become reality, so we must hold thoughts of what we want with passion. The moment we start our old self-defeating thought patterns is the moment we short-circuit our goals. One strategy that works for me is to use the "emotional hunger" mechanism as a cue to go inside and say "Ah, something is out of balance. Thank you, hunger mechanisms, for reminding me that I need to invoke my healing practices to breathe, go inside, and find out what is out of balance." Alternatively, I can give thanks, put some energy into what I really want. Think, visualize, daydream about WHAT I DO REALLY WANT.

The time we spend obsessing about that perfect body, the time we spend in self-loathing creates precisely what we don't want. Frustration over a piece of clothing that doesn't fit comes back as eating something highly caloric. THOUGHTS BECOME REALITY. Whatever we invest our EE in will translate into reality. You have to understand this principle at a cellular level. It is the most powerful life skill of the healing process.

If you KNEW, without a doubt, that the amount of energy, passion, enthusiasm, and joy you devoted to thinking about what you wanted in your life would in fact manifest in your life, how would you spend your Emotional Energy? Consider this: every day we have the ability to change the course of humanity, to change our destiny, to make the planet a better place. That is how powerful we are! This is achieved by our Emotional Energy. However EE, like electricity, is positive or negative. If we spend EE longing for food or hating ourselves, what manifests in our lives will be directly proportional to that EE.

chapter 7 – learning to love the plateau

Once we acknowledge the power of our thoughts and emotions, a critical aspect of healing is to master the life skill of "Breaking the Flow," described on page 141. The moment we start thinking about food we must stop, breathe, smile, let it go, and bring forward positive thoughts of what we truly want: health, choices, movement, vitality, joy. This is CRITICAL to healing the emotional hunger. Without this profound change very little will be gained from this work. If we continue to think about, want, long for food, that emotional investment will continue to translate into the reality of what we are living today. A popular saying goes, "Insanity is doing the same thing and expecting different results." It's time to change the emotional and thought paradigm.

If you are interested in a more in-depth exploration of the Law of Attraction, the resources I recommend are The Starter Set of Abraham-Hicks, which is a set of 5 CDs and/or *The Secret* DVD.

progress, not perfection

As you can see, we set milestones, not goals etched in stone. We are all different. We have different issues, different bodies, different emotional triggers, different resources, and different needs. This is profound, life-changing work. The goal of this program is progress, not perfection. If we are making progress every day, even in tiny increments, we are developing powerful life skills, we are on track.

Consider how we learn to walk and hold that image as you embark on this journey. A baby first learns how to roll onto its stomach. Then it learns to crawl and does this for several months. In fact, if the baby doesn't crawl and starts standing up too soon, studies show that it is detrimental to brain development. The baby then learns to stand up while holding on to something. After a few times of successfully executing the feat of just standing up, the baby takes one step and falls down. Can you imagine the results if the baby were to say to herself, "To hell with this! I keep falling down and hurting myself. I'm just going to crawl for the rest of my life." Thankfully, that doesn't happen; the baby keeps trying every day, and very slowly there are more steps, and more falls. Then one day, as if by magic, the baby walks.

- If you are eating better this week than last week, you are making progress
- If you are exercising more this week, you are making progress

- If you are able to recognize your emotions more effectively this week, you are making progress
- If you are able to sit with your emotions longer this week, you are making progress
- If you made a seven-day plan of nutritious meals to eat this week and you didn't last week, you are making progress
- If you have more vitality this week, you are making progress
- If you lose any weight at all this week, you are making progress!
- If you lose just one centimeter this week, you are making progress
- If you are able to do more reps for any of your exercises this week, you are making progress
- If you congratulate yourself and feel happy about making the smallest increments in your quest to be healthy, you are making progress
- If you learn to love one more aspect of yourself, you are making progress

You have at least 20 different opportunities to experience progress in this program:

1. How well you are eating and how it makes you feel better about yourself
2. How much more vitality you have in your daily life
3. How in touch with your emotions you are becoming
4. How you are learning to love every aspect of yourself
5. How you are consistently exercising
6. How you are learning new skills, such as meditation, that allow you to gain the benefits of low stress and peace of mind – benefits that improve the quality of your life
7. How you are able to be with your emotions until they dissipate
8. How you are learning to omit from your life people and activities that do not contribute to your well being
9. How your clothes are fitting better
10. How you are learning to make yourself a priority, and by being THE priority, improving the quality of your life
11. How you are learning to be a better mother/father, husband/wife, friend, or co-worker because you are better able to deal with your emotions

chapter 7 – learning to love the plateau

12. How you are improving the overall quality of your life because you are dealing with your emotions, lowering your stress, eating better, and feeling more vital
13. How you are getting to know yourself better as you develop the activities that support self-love
14. How you are learning to be a better mate/wife/lover because you are more accepting of your partner's shortcomings, and how you are relieving your mate of responsibility for your happiness
15. How you are learning to use the tools that help you with emotional eating
16. How you are acquiring tools such as the Oxygen Cocktail to enable you to deal more effectively with difficult situations in life
17. How you are preparing nutritious and healthy meals for yourself
18. How you are growing as a complete human being
19. How you are learning to be your own best advocate
20. How you are embracing the knowledge that happiness is your birthright

Don't let an inanimate piece of equipment like a scale determine how good you are going to feel about yourself and, by extension, about the quality of your life. Celebrate your progress! Berating yourself because you are not where you want to be today can cause you to give up the journey and start overeating again.

Denounce the mentality of instant gratification. Learn how to love small steps in the right direction. Celebrate the fact that you are committed to being your own best advocate. Learn from your mistakes – they have as much to teach you as your successes. Reaffirm that you are not going back and that you refuse to have your life force drained from you! Reaffirm that you are choosing to use all your resources to have the vitality you want. Reaffirm that you are committed to having a higher quality of life.

Learn to celebrate every single step you make, no matter how small. There are no insignificant steps. Keep recognizing: "If I lose a pound every week, I will be 52 pounds lighter a year from now, and those pounds are never coming back."

Dilia De La Altagracia

divide and conquer

This work is about learning self-love and developing critical life skills that will allow us to be with our emotions. For many of us the number of conditioned responses might be more than a few. Consequently certain periods of our lives may be spent addressing one particular suppressed aspect of ourselves. For example, one of my issues was the loneliness I felt when I came home to an empty house. My pattern was to turn on the TV and eat something. So for a few weeks all I worked on was coming home, being with my loneliness, and really feeling it until it no longer masked itself as hunger. Automatically, without conflict or negotiation, I saw no need to waste my precious time watching TV and eating food to avoid feeling lonely.

Once I had faced, felt, and finally integrated my loneliness, I realized that I liked being with myself and pursuing my interests. I also had many friends that I wanted to contact, and an evolutionary process began that led to relating to people and developing meaningful relationships. The important thing to remember is that it was I who changed. My qualities had always been there, my interests were always there, my friends were always there. But I needed to experience my loneliness, to embrace the negativity I felt about being alone and not wanting to admit that I was feeling lonely. Until that happened, my "hunger" was always there.

I devoted another period to focusing on ordering a wholesome meal when I went out to a restaurant. My suppressed feelings of inadequacy made me want to do things that would make other people like me. And what makes a waiter like you more than ordering a large, expensive meal and tipping lavishly? Once I came to terms with my feelings of inadequacy I began to honor myself, and then I ordered meals that contributed to my well being. I was totally oblivious of how others felt about my choices. The reality is that the waiter or waitress might react to a patron who is ordering a cheap meal, but, in most cases, they really don't care. We always have the option of leaving a good tip, once we overcome our feelings of inadequacy.

In another period, I focused on cooking healthful meals for myself without eating a full meal during their preparation. To achieve this goal, I had to sit with the anxiety I usually felt while cooking. I had to trust the recipe and promise myself that if, after I served the meal it needed something, I would fix it then. Once I learned to breathe

168

through the anxiety and be with it, I no longer needed to eat one full portion before the meal was served.

Next, I worked on refusing to over commit. I began by clearing my schedule. There is a wonderful quote from Thomas Merton about the abuse of over commitment: "To allow oneself to be carried away by a multitude of conflicting concerns, to surrender to too many demands, to commit oneself to too many projects, to want to help everyone in everything is to succumb to violence."

An important lesson I learned through all these steps is that my overeating behavior did not change as a result of some brilliant intellectual problem solving. Even though my Western, analytical mind always wanted to be in charge of finding "the solution," my best ideas and inspirations came from simply sitting with previously suppressed emotions. It's ironic that this tactic of tuning in to emotions was exactly what I'd learned to despise in other people as a sign of weakness. It was not cool to admit that I was lonely; it was not OK to say that I felt overwhelmed. My God, I was a world-class project manager – I could handle anything! And it was definitely not OK to feel anxious when I was supposed to be an unflappable person who could meet any commitment, no matter what. There's a certain sense in which Eastern humility serves us better than Western bravado. Sometimes surrender is the path to true victory.

conditioned response

Most people are aware of the famous experiments in which Ivan Pavlov, M.D., studied how reflexes are conditioned in the autonomic nervous system. Dr. Pavlov demonstrated that once dogs were trained to associate hearing a bell with being fed, even after the feedings were stopped the dogs salivated whenever they heard the bell. Dr. Pavlov's experiments proved that once we acquire a conditioned response to a stimulus, it takes counter-training to eradicate it. Most addictions have a compulsive, automatic aspect.

I had developed conditioned eating behaviors in response to the stimulus of unwanted emotions. Even after being present to my emotional triggers, I found it critical to deal with the many environmental stimuli not directly related to suppressed emotions.

home

For the longest time I couldn't understand why I was hungry when I got home, even after I had just eaten a wonderful dinner with friends. But when I ate with friends, I adhered to all the social protocols, and even though I indulged in three courses – salad, an entree and dessert – I was not a pig; I ate within the boundary of socially acceptable behavior. What I didn't acknowledge to myself was the "comfort" of eating at the frantic pace that I desired, without the damned constraints of protocol. Eating by myself meant complete freedom, and it was the only way to satisfy my need to relax or to avoid the emotional state of loneliness. Until I understood this correlation, I was doomed to repeat the self-destructive cycle.

Most compulsive overeating or bingeing is done at home. These are private rituals that require the safety of being alone, undisturbed, in my own castle, unconstrained by social protocol or external demands. For me it was critical to understand my need to feel soothed as soon as I parked my car. My need for security had to be uncoupled from the impulse to eat the moment I walked through the door. I had to develop a new set of behaviors to experience the soothing comfort I had associated with eating the moment I arrived home.

eating in the car

Eating in the car has become socially acceptable in the United States. It provides a controlled environment and many of the attributes of bingeing at home. Like home, it is another place where we are alone, and it creates that sense of freedom, of relief from social judgment and oppression.

television

William Dietz of the New England Medical Center and Steven Gortmaker of the Harvard School of Public Health found that obese children did not differ significantly from normal weight children in terms of friends, alone time, radio, reading, or leisure activities. But they did watch more television. Television is strongly associated with snacking; it is a sedentary, escapist response to life's problems and a large portion of the commercials glamorize eating.

chapter 7 – learning to love the plateau

I finally realized that if the only way I can watch a TV program is by putting something in my mouth, then obviously the show itself is not that interesting. I drew a line in the sand and finally asked, "Is this program interesting enough to watch without having to consume a few hundred calories?" It is rare that there is something so interesting on that I can watch it without eating. The moment I want to eat something is the moment I turn off the TV. I now know that I would rather do something else.

thinness worship

"As leanness has been increasingly prized, Americans have actually become fatter."

–Bennett and Gurin

Cutting down exposure to mass media helps minimize the stress and self-loathing that we experience when we don't measure up to beauty icons. Cindy Crawford, one of the healthiest influences on beauty, is also a woman secure enough to say, "I don't look as good as my photographs." We forget that the final photographs that are depicted in magazines are a result of hours of work by gifted makeup artists, lighting personnel, photographers and graphic artists. Once the photographs are generated, they are air brushed (or now computer-doctored) to remove any imperfections. If you don't believe that, pay the $1,000 – not the $69.95 at some glamour-shot mall studio – for one of these companies to produce the best ever photograph of you. Somehow we think we have to live up to these fabrications and the work of an army of professionals. Granted, many of us can do better where personal appearance is concerned. But if we continue to stress over not being beautiful enough to be on the cover of a magazine, we are doomed to live insecure lives of nervous desperation. We can choose to stress ourselves, or we can show up as the most attractive person we can be. The choice is ours. Would you prefer to marry a GQ or Vogue model who is egotistical, uncaring, and has no clue about what makes you happy? Or would you opt for an average-looking partner who is loving, caring, and concerned about your well-being? I would venture to say that most of us would choose the latter.

food as the basis for friendship

A study conducted by Garn and associates found that "People living with fat people tend to become fat and this generalization applies to

171

dogs and cats and even birds as well." If friendships are based solely on meeting for lunch or dinner as opposed to just being with someone to share hurts, triumphs, or feelings, or for activities such as hiking, skiing, or anything physical, then we can't help but be fat. If food is the only way we can express, "I care about you," how can that belief system contribute to a healthy lifestyle?

lunch break

During the workweek, I ate at my desk. I rationalized it as a means of saving time. As a single mother, I needed every minute of the day. Eating at my desk meant that I could go home 40 minutes earlier. I was a very efficient eater. I could go downstairs, select what I wanted to eat, pay for it and be back at my desk in 12 minutes. Then I could plow through a significant amount of food in eight minutes. I had no clue that taking the time to eat with a co-worker or a friend would relieve me of the need to bulldoze through the food. Yes, I had heard that eating slower would be helpful and it would "tell my brain that I was full." The reality was that I needed to calm down emotionally. Gorging through lunch helped me relax and seemed to provide the relief I needed to get back to work and put in another intense four hours before it was time to go home to my second job of being a single mom.

I never verbalized these feelings; I never complained about my life. I was never a whiner, nor did I respect those people who were. I saw myself as a positive, can-do, "kick-ass" worker and a dependable friend who was always there to help others. I never saw the wisdom of taking an hour to unwind from the stress of the first half of a very hectic morning instead of overeating to relieve the stress. I never realized that I was eating alone to get my emotional 'fix' so I could take on the rest of the day.

dealing with setbacks

"People are like stained glass windows. They sparkle and shine when the sun is out, but when the darkness sets in, their true beauty is revealed only if there is a light from within."

– Elisabeth Kübler-Ross

When I truly began to deal with my overeating behavior, each setback was an opportunity to revisit my progress and ask: "What lesson do I need to learn from this experience?" It also gave me the chance to

chapter 7 – learning to love the plateau

reaffirm my desire to be healthy, not to overeat or over commit, and not to place other people's needs ahead of my own. It allowed me to revisit my loneliness and desire to love myself.

I also learned that it was a long journey. Instead of using each setback as another event that demonstrated how unworthy and unlovable I was, or to allow a return of the hateful self-talk I had always engaged in, I learned to accept them as part of my path – as being human. I finally stopped beating myself up over the setbacks and strived for "consistency not perfection" – 80% of the time, not 100% of the time. Every setback was an opportunity to understand what I needed to adjust, how vigilant I had to be about meeting my needs and how I was creating a new paradigm – a new way of living – in which I was the most important person on my priority list. I was charting new territory for myself and eradicating old, deeply rooted belief systems.

long-term investment

While I was writing this book, a friend stopped by for dinner. He had begun his diet at 350 pounds and had lost 46 pounds in ten weeks. He was being good and feeling successful. I had invited him to come over and have stir-fry, which consisted of vegetables and about 6 ounces of lean steak. He asked me if I could cook his meal without oil. Sure, of course. I set up two frying pans, one for me, which contained two tablespoons of light olive oil, and one for my friend without oil. While cooking mine, I also added some soy sauce, which my friend also asked me to skip for him. While I was very willing to comply with his requests, and I admired his determination and willpower, I also remembered when I had been just as strict about what I ate, and how it never lasted, as long as I was simply following a diet with no consciousness of my deeper needs.

My calculations indicated that I had eaten 150 more calories than my friend, but the significant difference was not in the calories: I had enjoyed my dinner thoroughly, and I could live eating this way for the rest of my life. On the other hand, I wasn't sure my friend could sustain his self-deprivation for many more weeks. And that is the failure of all diets. Whatever eating regimen you choose, you should be ready to follow it, to learn to select ingredients and cook them according to that philosophy, for the rest of your life.

Eating is a pleasure in life. Except under the most extreme medical conditions, it is rare to encounter people who want to give up the

173

pleasure of eating. So the questions each one of us must answer are, "What is realistic for me? How can I eat in a healthy fashion for the rest of my life? Once I stop eating my emotions, what is the balance between being incredibly disciplined – that is, eating to nurture my body only – and being selective and judicious while still enjoying the pleasure of eating?" Yes, we can make very restrictive choices, but one in 10 million people can actually live this way for the rest of their lives. My recollection is that when I embarked on these restrictive diets, I was elated about my progress for the first few weeks. But I soon craved the pleasures of eating, and off to oblivion went the diet.

It takes longer to lose weight when one is being judicious versus being perfect, but it is a life-changing commitment versus a short-term mirage. It is only human to want to lose weight as quickly as possible, but we desire to lose weight, keep it off, and maintain a healthy weight for the rest of our lives. The scientific studies indicate that any loss achieved through heroic means will not last. Anytime we eat in a restrictive manner, our progress will be offset as soon as we return to eating normally. The challenge is to start eating judiciously and intelligently and to be able to say with truth and joy, "I could eat this way for the rest of my life."

OK, but what should you eat? First, let me give you an example of what people who are not emotional eaters eat.

- Breakfast: 2 free range eggs fried in light olive oil, with 3 oz of chicken sausage.
- Snack: 4 pieces of sugar free extra rich dark chocolate with coffee – no sugar
- Dinner: Protein Salad. Protein could be cashew, or seasoned tofu or a few ounces of fish, chicken or lean meat with one glass of wine.
- Bottled, spring or filtered water throughout the day

To an emotional overeater, the above example might seem meager and unrealistic, but for those who don't have an emotional eating problem, it's entirely satisfying. The point is that once food stops being the driving force in your life, you will be amazed at how little food you really need to function in a healthy and joyous manner.

To repeat, once food is no longer the way you deal with the stresses and emotional challenges of life, you can choose your nutritional objective

chapter 7 – learning to love the plateau

– athletic performance, longevity, or food pleasure – and your consumption will vary depending on your objectives and activity level. You will know that you are not driven by food when:

- You sit down at the dinner table to eat your meals.
- Eating activities and eating times are not the highlights of your day.
- You can sit and watch a TV program without eating.
- You do not obsess about food.
- You can eat your meal and breathe deeply between bites.
- You can eat slowly and methodically.
- You do not feel deprived if you are not able to partake in a sumptuous buffet.
- You do not measure the joy of your day by what you will eat that day.
- Though you still take pleasure in healthy, well-prepared food, you no longer have to gorge to feel fulfilled.
- Food is not the way to measure most of your pleasure in life.
- You would rather savor a banana bite by bite than rush through a buffet.
- You can schedule an enjoyable activity with a friend that doesn't include eating.

the long journey

80 pounds of impatience

After the first month of euphoria, and experiencing some wonderful changes in my life, I had to settle into the reality of the journey. After the big changes stopped happening, and the plateaus got longer and longer, I had to find contentment week after week with very small weight loss. I had to restate my desire to be healthy and my unwillingness to go back to destructive behaviors. For the first three months I had to reaffirm every single day my desire not to overeat. For the first three months I had to make myself write down everything – everything – that I ate every single day. There were perfect days in terms of what I ate and how much I exercised, yet I still didn't see any difference in my appearance, and it made me feel desperate. I wanted change NOW. I had to keep repeating, "You have 80 pounds of impatience. Remember, you are making progress; you are losing one to two pounds a week, and it is a change for the rest of your life – for the rest of your life."

Some of my questions about staying on the journey were, "What makes some people stick to the path when others give up? Why do some people see things through to completion while others give up within weeks?" There has been some fascinating research in this field, some of which can be found in *The Truth About Addiction and Recovery* by Stanton Peele and Archie Brodsky.

As I've said, however, this work is not about the mind. It is about our emotions. When I became discouraged because I was not seeing the reflection I wanted in the mirror, and I didn't want to continue the program, I had to listen for the umpteenth time to my tape on affirmations and visualizations. Sometimes I had to breathe and consider the dismal alternative to continuing the program. When I started feeling impatient I would do yoga, specifically the forward bend and then the camel. To help with my frustration, I wrote in my journal. Fortunately, I was able to recognize the frustration, and I had the ability to be with it. Very slowly, food ceased to be my preferred solution; I no longer wanted to eat unconsciously – to eat my frustration.

At certain times when you are following the program, you will become frustrated because you don't seem to be making progress. First, it is important to acknowledge that this is normal. Second, sit with your feelings. If you need help, breathe into the energy center that is out of balance. Do the corresponding yoga posture, journal, meditate, and keep breathing deeply. Experience the disappointment of being good but still not getting where you want to be. Experience the frustration of how long this seems to be taking. But also consider the alternatives. This same principle applies to any process that has the power to truly transform ones life.

Whenever I wanted to overeat, I had to go inside again to find out what was happening. Many times there were unexpressed emotions. I had such difficulty asking for what I needed, what I paid for, what I wanted. It amazed me how seemingly small events would manifest themselves as emotional hunger. I had to sit and breathe deeply, or listen to my visualization and affirmation tape, or run to my computer and start writing whenever I wanted to eat through these emotions. I kept thinking that the issue was some event, but in many cases it was deeper. It was an issue of self-love and self-expression, of knowing that I was worthwhile and coming to understand that I was worth the love from within myself.

chapter 7 – learning to love the plateau

The journey began as a desire to lose weight. It evolved into a new and deeper perception of the quality of my entire life. In the end, the journey was about love, especially learning to love myself.

"God breaks the heart again and again and again ... until it stays open."

- Hazrat Inayat Khan

The above quote is one of my all time favorites. I finally understood why members of Alcoholic Anonymous, years after they have stopped drinking, still introduce themselves as 'alcoholic.' While we want to heal the emotional hunger and invest all of this misguided energy into something creative, life affirming, and joyous, we must also acknowledge that when we encounter any situation that disrupts our emotional balance, we are very likely to go back to our learned coping mechanism, which, in our case, is overeating.

Despite the fact that there are hundreds of little tricks we may employ to lose weight, the goal is not to accumulate more tricks. Emotional healing occurs when we can be centered, whole, present, and not defeated by events in our lives.

living from the life force

If the prospect of being comfortable in your own skin doesn't excite you, if living fully and deeply does not appeal to you more than the next slice of cheesecake, then the behaviors that are necessary to maintain a healthy body weight will elude you. Once you learn how to be with your emotions, it is not a struggle to say no to food that weighs you down physically. If saying no continues to be a struggle, you have not truly learned to be with your feelings, and the emotional residue is still fueling the hunger and the compulsive overeating. If being with your emotions is sporadic, then more than likely you will be seduced by the next major diet on the market, by the next promise of magical thinness. You have to be able to be present and aware of your emotions at all times and in any place, and you need to have the ability to be with those emotions without eating them.

Once I learned how to be with myself, and I started being present with all my emotions – not just the wonderful stuff in my life but also the loneliness, the boredom, the disappointment, the anger – I stopped overeating. Having the ability to be with my emotions has allowed me access to resources that I always had but was never able to call upon when emotional hunger manifested itself. I can now access these resources to deal with the reality of my life. I do not live some happily-ever-after fairy tale as a result of no longer eating compulsively. My soul mate didn't magically materialize the moment I lost weight. My problems didn't disappear. But all of the energy and all of the shame that went into showing up for my life FAT was channeled into living as fully as possible, as humanly as possible. I am not this society's idea of a cover model. I am not a size zero or two, but neither am I overweight. No longer do I eat compulsively, and it is truly wonderful to feel comfortable in my own skin. It is exhilarating to have a man find me sexy. It is my ultimate freedom to move how I want, to wear what I want, to go where I want, and to experience freely and joyfully what I want to experience. No longer are my activities restricted because I'm carrying 80 pounds of extra weight. No longer am I stopped by the shame of imagining how I will look in a bathing suit, a fancy gown, or a simple pair of jeans. I can just show up, be present, and truly enjoy the activities and events that life presents. I am finally able to live fully! Ask yourself: What is your quality of life? How will you feel physically when you are not carrying that extra weight? What would change if shame vanished from your life? How would you feel if you could choose your activities based on your desires and not your limitations? To what are you willing to say no in order to realize this deeper consciousness, these healthier options? What would it mean if you loved yourself?

Now you know the steps: First, be with your emotions. Next, let self-love guide you to wise choices. Finally, choose to embrace life and live fully. All you need to do is to take action, begin today.

Appendix

appendix a: how to meditate

We will start with breath meditation. What is breath meditation? It is any type of meditation in which we focus attention on our breathing.

the technique

1. Practice mindfulness of the breath. Do not control the breath; instead, allow it to occur in its natural cadence and depth. While breathing, focus on:
   - The flow of air (as it goes past the tips of the nostrils, the insides of the nostrils, the throat, and into the lungs)
   - The abdomen's motion (inward and outward)
   - The sound of the breath
   - The pause after each exhalation — a state of silence, with no thoughts
   - The quality of the air (perhaps its coolness or its scent)
   - The spontaneous rhythm of the exhalations and inhalations
   - The uniqueness of each breath (the speed, depth, or other characteristics)
   - The various sensations throughout the torso as the lungs expand and contract
   - The unity with the breath process (you might feel that you are "being breathed" instead of being a separate witness to the process)
2. Count each breath. Try these variations:
   - Count the number of heartbeats for the inhalations, exhalations, and pauses. For example, count 1-2-3-4 during the inhalation; then 1-2-3-4-5 during the exhalation; then 1-2-3 during the pause. Do not control the breath; allow it to proceed at its natural pace while counting.
   - Count "one" for the first inhalation; "two" for the next inhalation; "three" for the next inhalation; etc. (Do not count the exhalations.) Or count only the exhalations, without counting the inhalations.

- Count "one" for the inhalation; "two" for the exhalation. Then repeat "one" for the next inhalation and "two" for the next exhalation, etc. (Do not count beyond the number "two.")

3. "Note" the breath. In noting meditation, say a word that names the action; this practice helps to concentrate on the action. For example:
   - Think the word "inhale" when inhaling; think the word "exhale" when exhaling
   - When concentrating on the corresponding movement of the abdomen, the words would be "rising" and "falling," or "out" and "in"
   - Simply think the word "breathing" during each inhalation or during each exhalation, or during both the inhalation and exhalation

4. Think particular words while inhaling. Those words can be a mantra, any phrase, or a self-talk statement. While exhaling:
   - Think the mantra or phrase again
   - Say the mantra, phrase, or statement aloud
   - Ponder the meaning of the sentence, phrase, or statement.

5. Visualize the breath
   - During each inhalation, visualize energy or light, or something positive coming into you. During exhalation, visualize something "negative" (e.g., stress, physical pain, emotional disturbances, or other unwanted conditions) passing from you or something "positive" (e.g., blessings or love) being sent out into the world).
   - When inhaling, visualize life-energy entering the lungs. In each subsequent inhalation, visualize a larger amount of life energy entering.
   - When inhaling, visualize life-energy traveling to a particular part of the body, for instance, the brain, heart, or a painful ankle. When exhaling, see the tension or pain leaving that body part.
   - During inhalation, visualize life-energy entering from a source other than the air; this source might be the sun, the earth, or another nurturing source.
   - Visualize the entire body participating in the respiratory process. Every cell is exchanging its carbon dioxide for life-enhancing oxygen.

6. Have the eyes open slightly, so that some light can enter. When inhaling, feel the energy of this light entering into the body. During exhalation, feel the energy circulating throughout the body.
7. Gaze at an object — physical or visualized — that symbolizes beauty or peace or another quality you want to develop. When inhaling, feel the quality of that object entering; while exhaling, respond by sending that same quality back to the object. Eventually, your attention might transcend this duality of yourself and the object; instead, you become more aware of the quality itself and the empty space in which that quality exists.

appendix b: special needs

Throughout this book, I have stated that the very first step is to get in touch with your emotions. I was so out of touch with mine that I couldn't even conceive that they had anything to do with overeating. For those of us with a history of difficulties recognizing our emotions — whether because we were neglected as children, because we always put other people's needs ahead of our own, or because we have a history of difficulty saying no to others — having access to our emotions might be neither an intuitive nor a simple matter. So in doing this program I had the added burden of removing the blockage that impeded access to my feelings.

I began to have a hint that there was a problem recognizing my emotions after going to an eating disorder physiologist and feeling stumped when asked, "What do you feel when you are overeating?" I then realized that I was unaware of my own feelings and that I needed help with just getting in touch with my emotions. This led to research and trial and error to find out what tools would allow me to do so. After going to therapists and reading about emotional issues, the search for getting in touch with my feelings led me to therapeutic massage, Reiki and Core Energetics.

benefits of massage therapy

The following is an article titled *What is Massage Therapy?*[11] written by Cherri Straus, MPH. I highly recommend massage as one of the modalities to get in touch with the correlation between body sensations and our feelings.

Dilia De La Altagracia

What is Massage Therapy?

Massage therapy is a procedure that uses touch to manipulate the soft body tissues to increase health and well-being. The benefits of massage have been recognized since ancient times. The ancient Greeks referred to it as "rubbing." Massage was also used by the ancient Egyptians, Romans, and Chinese. The Greeks and Romans always included a massage as part of their daily exercise and bathing rituals. The current type of massage therapy came about in the nineteenth century in Sweden and is known as Swedish massage.

Massage involves a manual application of pressure and movement to soft body tissues — the skin, muscles, tendons, ligaments, and fascia (membranes surrounding muscles). Massage is believed to increase blood circulation and the flow of lymph (fluid from body tissues that flows into the blood stream). It helps the body to "heal itself" by promoting the flow of blood and lymph, stimulating nerves, conditioning the skin, and stretching and loosening muscles to keep them elastic. Massage also has a positive psychological effect. When we are stressed, our breathing becomes more rapid and shallow, our hearts work harder and digestion slows down. Chronic stress can influence a number of illnesses including migraines, depression, and hypertension. Massage therapy can help to relieve tension and counteract the effects of stress on the body.

There are dozens of specialized massage techniques in use today. The most common types are:
- Swedish Massage – uses long strokes, kneading and pressing, friction, and drumming hand movements applied to the muscle groups to promote circulation and relaxation. This technique is often used for a full body massage
- Deep Tissue Massage – uses deep finger pressure and slow strokes on aching or tense areas of the body
- Sports Massage – uses massage to prepare the body before exercise or to help the body recover after exercise. It focuses on the use of massage to assist training, prevent injury, and treat sports injuries
- Shiatsu/Acupressure Massage – uses pressure at specific points on the body with the Eastern philosophical belief that this will enhance the energy flow through the body and restore balance

appendix

- Neuromuscular Massage (also called Trigger-point Therapy) – uses finger pressure on painful areas in muscles called trigger points
- Reflexology – uses pressure points in the hands and feet to affect reflexes in other parts of the body

I had a weekly massage for a period of seven months. I found the massages helpful and relaxing. One of my friends once said that it is inhumane not be touched in an intimate way. As a fat woman, I believed no man that I was attracted to wanted to touch me in an intimate manner. I spent several years without physical contact. A good deep tissue massage is not a substitute for physical intimacy but it did help me begin the sensitization process.

Reiki: what is it and what are its benefits?

Reiki ("universal life energy" in Japanese) involves a very light, gentle pattern of touch over the clothed body, originating from and directed by the flow of Ki, rather than by the practitioner's own energy. The word Ki in Japanese is the same as the Chinese word "Chi," as in Tai Chi or Chi Kung.

Reiki is a form of touch therapy that offers deep relaxation, inner peace, and a quiet mind. It is also complementary to traditional health care for physical problems, because it redirects the flow of energy, bringing balance to the emotional and physical body and producing inner harmony. Perhaps the most profound effects of Reiki are seen in its ability to support and facilitate self-awareness.

Several medical studies on Reiki therapy show that it produces a significant reduction in perceived anxiety, an increase in immunological functioning, a significant drop in systolic blood pressure, and a decrease in pain, which reduces the necessity for medications.

Medical research also observes that Reiki:
- Activates life force energy
- Is non-invasive with no side-effects
- Significantly increases hemoglobin levels

- Creates feelings of peacefulness and safety, with recipients reporting experiences of increased calm and relaxation.

Medical doctors and registered nurses who have studied Reiki therapy note that its focus is overall wellness and prevention of disease; reduction of anxiety, muscle tension, and systolic blood pressure; and significant increase in immunoglobulin-A. This energy-based system has endless potential and can be useful in any medical setting to aid in healing the body both emotionally and physically.

One California study showed that Reiki can increase hemoglobin and hematocrit levels. The study compared 47 people participating in Reiki training and a small control group of nine healthy medical professionals. The study found a significant increase in hemoglobin and hematocrit levels among the Reiki group and no significant change in the control group.

Reiki energy equals radiance, renewal, and well-being, giving inner and outer beauty and light to the mind, body, and spirit.

Full-body Reiki is used holistically to achieve deep relaxation. It facilitates the removal of blockages in energy flow and the dispersal of toxins.

I went to a Reiki therapist for approximately four months and found the sessions relaxing and helpful. Additional information about Reiki can be found in Barbara Brennan and Jos. A. Smith's book, Hands of Lights.

benefit of bio- or Core Energetics

After going to the Reiki therapist, I was then willing to investigate alternative healing practices and began to study how the body/mind connection has been a fundamental part of Eastern psychological theory for thousands of years. I first tried the recent Western healing versions of body/mind psychology. Of these, Bioenergetics and Core Energetics are the two most recent Western manifestations of mind/body therapies. I went to a Core Energetics therapist for approximately five months. The visits were very different from the traditional Western psychologists with whom you only express your feelings in the form of physical expression, mostly in the form of hitting something to express hostilities, which, ultimately, will make us fatter). I was also encouraged to express my sensations when I was feeling hungry. I honestly had a difficult time getting in touch with these sensations. The Core Energetics sessions were expensive, inconvenient and finally, for me personally, ineffective. Although the concepts are well grounded, the specific Core Energetics therapist that I consulted engaged in too much analysis, which my Western mind adored, but in contrast to my current yoga practice, had very little bodywork. Because of the expense, I was not able to attend these sessions but for two hours per month. Once I started yoga, first in an effort to get a physical workout but later with the understanding that it would help me get in touch with my emotions, I was doing twenty-four hours a month at half the cost of one Core Energetics therapy session. More important, once I was able to do the yoga postures, I was beginning to feel the difference in my ability to get in touch with my emotions.

Please understand that I'm not discrediting Core Energetics. If you have the financial means and are seeing a therapist anyway, Core Energetics might be very effective for you. What I personally experienced was that yoga was substantially more helpful in getting in touch with my feelings than Core Energetics. This might be a function of the therapist or my own personal development. But after doing so much head work, I needed the emotional release that only bodywork, in my case yoga, facilitated.

It is critical to ask yourself, "Am I in touch with my emotions? Do I really feel what is going on in my body right before I plunge into the despair of bingeing? Can I truly express what is bothering me right before overeating?" If you are lucky enough to be in touch with your emotions, then bodywork might not be as critical to you as it was for me. Maybe you might have security issues, self-esteem issues, expression issues — the list of what keeps us from being fully aware is fairly long — and what is important is that your specific issues be addressed. The point is that you might need help in addressing whatever issues are blocking your ability to get in touch with your emotions. If, on the other hand, you are not in touch with your emotions, then bodywork — not exercise, not more headwork/psycho-babble — is critical in helping you remove whatever is blocking access to your emotions. Until we are in touch with our emotions, we cannot feel "I'm tired, I'm bored, I'm lonely, I'm disappointed" and at the very least begin being with those emotions and, in a sense, creating a detour instead of an express lane to the refrigerator.

I have outlined therapies that I have personally tried out to get in touch with my emotions. Consequently, the list is short, and there is just four of the alternative kind. There are scores of therapies to unblock suppressed emotions and to help us remove emotional blocks or sensitize ourselves to our emotions. A great reference is a book by Mirka Knaster titled *Discovering The Body's Wisdom: A Comprehensive Guide To More Than Fifty Mind-Body Practices That Can Relieve Pain Reduce Stress, And Foster Health, Spiritual Growth, And Inner Peace.* Some of these alternative therapies might be more effective than those that I tried during my personal journey. We are not all the same; you must try everything for yourself and honor that which works for you.